Experiments for
General Chemistry I

CENGAGE
Learning·

Australia · Brazil · Japan · Korea · Mexico · Singapore · Spain · United Kingdom · United States

Experiments for General Chemistry I

Executive Editor:
Michael Stranz

Managing Lab Editor:
Cydney Capell

Custom Lab Editors:

Custom Production Editor:
Jennifer Flinchpaugh

Project Coordinators:
Lisa Donahue. Peg Hagar

Senior Pre-Press Specialist:
Kathy Paxton

Production Supervisor-Labs:
Melanie Evans

Rights and Permissions Specialist:
Kalina Ingham Hintz

Senior Marketing Specialist:
Sara Mercurio

For product information and technology assistance, contact us at
Cengage Learning Customer & Sales Support, 1-800-354-9706

For permission to use material from this text or product,
submit all requests online at **cengage.com/permissions**
Further permissions questions can be emailed to
permissionrequest@cengage.com

ISBN-13: 978-1-4240-8362-6

ISBN-10: 1-4240-8362-1

Cengage Learning
5191 Natorp Blvd.
Mason, OH 45040
USA

Cengage Learning is a leading provider of customized learning solutions with office locations around the globe, including Singapore, the United Kingdom, Australia, Mexico, Brazil, and Japan. Locate your local office at:
international.cengage.com/region

Cengage Learning products are represented in Canada by Nelson Education, Ltd.

Visit Signature Labs online at **signaturelabs.com**

Visit our corporate website at **cengage.com**

Printed in the United States of America

Acknowledgements

The content of this text has been adapted from the following product(s):

Acids And Bases: Analysis - Murov
ISBN-10: (0-495-25295-6)
ISBN-13: (978-0-495-25295-5)

Measurements And Identification Techniques - Murov
ISBN-10: (0-495-25274-3)
ISBN-13: (978-0-495-25274-0)

STOI0906: Determining Hydrogen Peroxide Content by Gas Stoichiometry
ISBN-10: (0-53497-768-5)
ISBN-13: (978-0-53497-768-9)

Lewis Structures And Molecular Models - Murov
ISBN-10: (0-495-25287-5)
ISBN-13: (978-0-495-25287-0)

Molecular Polarity And Chromatography - Murov
ISBN-10: (0-495-25288-3)
ISBN-13: (978-0-495-25288-7)

Cooling Curves And Crystal Structures - Murov
ISBN-10: (0-495-25292-1)
ISBN-13: (978-0-495-25292-4)

Density, Accuracy, Precision And Graphing - Murov
ISBN-10: (0-495-25275-1)
ISBN-13: (978-0-495-25275-7)

Empirical Formulas - Murov
ISBN-10: (0-495-25278-6)
ISBN-13: (978-0-495-25278-8)

Classification Of Chemical Reactions - Murov
ISBN-10: (0-495-25276-X)
ISBN-13: (978-0-495-25276-4)

Quantitative Precipitation - Murov
ISBN-10: (0-495-25277-8)
ISBN-13: (978-0-495-25277-1)

Electrical Conductivity And Elecrolytes - Murov
ISBN-10: (0-495-25279-4)

ISBN-13: (978-0-495-25279-5)

Early Explorations And Terminology - Murov
ISBN-10: (0-495-25272-7)
ISBN-13: (978-0-495-25272-6)

Ionic Reactions - Murov
ISBN-10: (0-495-25280-8)
ISBN-13: (978-0-495-25280-1)

Separation Of Mixtures - Murov
ISBN-10: (0-495-25273-5)
ISBN-13: (978-0-495-25273-3)

Thermochemistry - Murov
ISBN-10: (0-495-25284-0)
ISBN-13: (978-0-495-25284-9)

Acids And Bases: Reactions And Standardization - Murov
ISBN-10: (0-495-25294-8)
ISBN-13: (978-0-495-25294-8)

SYNT0907: Applying the Concept of a Limiting Reactant to the Synthesis of Aspirin
ISBN-10: (0-534-97778-2)
ISBN-13: (978-0-534-97778-8)

Spectroscopy Of Cobalt (II) Ion - Murov
ISBN-10: (0-495-25286-7)
ISBN-13: (978-0-495-25286-3)

ANAL0909: Determining the Thickness of Zinc on Galvanized Washers
ISBN-10: (0-534-47998-7)
ISBN-13: (978-0-534-47998-5)

Table Of Contents

EARLY EXPLORATIONS AND TERMINOLOGY

1865 Bunsen burner

Learning Objectives

Upon completion of this experiment, students will have experienced:
1. Practice with techniques of observation and the scientific method.
2. The use of the Bunsen burner.
3. Basic glassworking.
4. Some basic chemistry terminology.

Text Topics

Scientific method, physical properties, chemical reactions (see page ix).

Notes to Students and Instructor

This experiment will probably take more than one laboratory period. It can be started on the first lab day which usually includes check-in procedures and a safety presentation and then finished on the second lab day. Alternatively, selection of only certain sections should shorten the experiment. *Most sections of this experiment should be thoroughly discussed in class after completion of the experiment.*

Discussion

Pretend for a moment that it is a very hot day. Use your imagination to visualize a glass of ice water. Have you noticed that the ice is floating in the water and not resting on the bottom of the glass? Has this observation ever puzzled you? *Observation and imagination are two of the keys to good science.* Mysteries that arise from inconsistencies between expectations and observations often contain clues that lead to exciting and wonderful discoveries.

Consider the ice-water system. What should happen to the density (mass/volume) of a liquid as it is cooled? We might expect a contraction of volume and an increase in density as the temperature decreases (resulting in sinking). And yet, contrary to this expectation, the ice is less dense than liquid water and floats. Included in the observation of the ice-water system then should be the unexpected floating of the ice and questions about why the ice floats and if it is common for the solid phase of a substance to float in its liquid.

Learn to make careful, complete and unbiased observations and include as part of these observations, questions on any inconsistencies that arise from them. Ideally observations should not depend on the observer as we are trying to **record facts in an understandable way for other people.** It is important that scientific observations be reproducible. The observation section of a report should not include interpretations or explanations because explanations might differ from one observer to the next and there may even be more than one possible conclusion. Ice sometimes forms with small air bubbles and in these cases one should record that there are air bubbles in the ice. But to say that the ice floats because of air bubbles is not an observation but in this case an inadequate explanation.

It is very important to record all observations as the act of disregarding or ignoring is actually a conclusion that an observation is not important. Some very important observations have been overlooked only to be found by later investigators to have significance (penicillin and nuclear fission are two examples). Discoveries of teflon and aspartame were made serendipitously by careful observers who did not overlook the unexpected. When doing science, pay heed to the words of Ralph Waldo Emerson, *"God hides things by putting them near us.,"* and Louis Pasteur, *"In the fields of observation, chance favors only the mind that is prepared."*

Observation is the first part of a process commonly called *the scientific method*. Although its emphasis in some textbooks sometimes gives the misleading impression that scientists operate according to a schedule, the scientific method does describe the process that occurs in scientific exploration. It starts with the puzzling observation and resulting questions. Next with the use of imagination, explanations (or hypotheses) are suggested. Fortunately in science (and this is what makes science easier than most fields), explanations are testable. If experiments support an explanation, the explanation becomes a theory. The theory is always subject to further testing which can result in modification or even discarding of the theory.

As you do your laboratory experiments, remember to stay alert and record all observations including questions about anything curious to you. Be sure that your records are written clearly and concisely in a way that can be understood and tested by others.

Procedure

This exercise has been designed to help you develop your observational skills, distinguish between observations and explanations, and to learn to carefully record all observations. Remember that complete observations often lead to questions.

A. The meniscus. Add water to about the half way point of a 50 mL graduated cylinder and study the features of the water surface. Describe and draw your observations. The phenomenon that you observe is called a meniscus. Write down a question about the meniscus. [Comment: Volumetric glassware has been calibrated to give correct volume measurements when you read the **very** bottom of the meniscus.]

B. The candle flame. Light a candle and study the flame. Write down all your observations and questions about the flame. Try to include observations on states of matter and physical and chemical properties and changes. Be very careful to distinguish observations from explanations. What do you think is actually burning? Write your answer down before you read or experiment further. You will not lose points for an incorrect answer.

Be sure to record observations from the following tests. Put a beaker over the burning candle almost but not all the way down and carefully observe the inside of the beaker. Blow the candle out and immediately put a glass stirring rod on top of the extinguished wick in the region where the flame had been. Inspect the rod. Relight the candle, and, with a burning match in one hand, again blow the candle out. Immediately bring the burning match to the region where the flame had been, moving the match slowly towards the wick for the last 2 cm. Save the candle for Part L.

C. The Bunsen burner. One of the important tools of the laboratory chemist is the Bunsen burner. This exercise has been designed to familiarize you with the burner and introduce you to glassworking. Study *Figure 1-1* and compare it to your Bunsen burner.

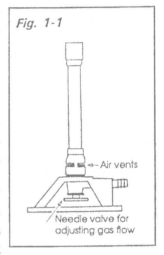

Fig. 1-1

<-- Air vents

Needle valve for adjusting gas flow

[Comment: The instructor should demonstrate use of the burner.] Close the air control and make sure the gas valve is off. Turn the gas valve on the bench on full, light a match, open the burner gas valve and light the gas. What color is it? Increase the gas flow until the flame is about 8 cm. high and open the air control until the yellow color is gone. Draw and describe the flame. What do you think is the hottest region? Take a wood splint and insert it quickly into the flame right over the top of the burner (*Figure 1-2*). Hold it there until it ignites and observe where it burns. Now hold a wire gauze vertically in the flame so that about 1 cm. of the gauze extends beyond the far edge of the burner (*Figure 1-3*). Heat it until it glows and record your observations about the position and pattern of glow. If significant amounts of colored flame leap from the gauze, rinse the corner of the gauze that you are heating with deionized water and repeat the test.

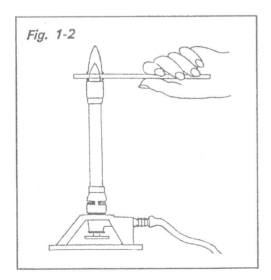

Fig. 1-2

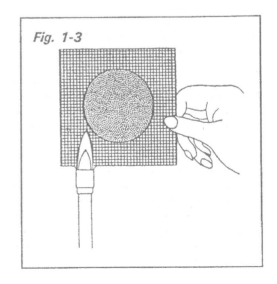

Fig. 1-3

Glassworking. Take a file and make a deep scratch on a piece of 6 mm glass tubing 20 cm from the end. Be sure not to make more than one groove. Holding the scratch away from you with thumbs on either side of the scratch, push your thumbs forward, pulling the two pieces apart (*Figure 1-4*). With a decent scratch, the glass will almost split by itself. However, the ends will still be sharp enough to cut you. Anytime glass tubing is cut, the ends should be firepolished to round off the sharp edges.

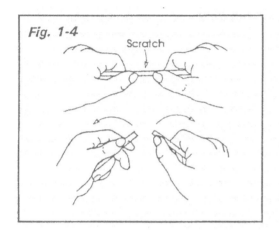

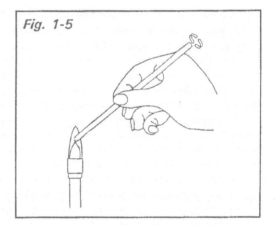

Firepolishing. Following *Figure 1-5*, hold the tubing at about 30° to the horizontal in the hottest part of the flame. Rotate the tubing and observe it carefully. As it approaches its melting point, a bright sodium flame will be observed. Continue to rotate it until it barely melts. Too much melting will begin to constrict the tube opening. Put the tubing down on a wire gauze until it has cooled and firepolish the other end (*Caution: One of the most common lab accidents is the burning of fingers and hands on glass that has been picked up without sufficient cooling.*)

Bending tubing. Chemists often have to make their own specialized pieces of glassware and it is very useful to have some experience with bending glass. Turn off the Bunsen burner and insert the flame spreader (often called a wing tip). Relight just as you did without the flame spreader and adjust the flame as in *Figure 1-6*. Hold both ends of the tube, place it in the hot region of the flame and rotate rapidly. A relatively even yellow glow indicates even heating. After the tube has softened, remove it from the flame, bend it to a right angle and hold it steady for a few seconds. Place it on the gauze for cooling. Do not be disappointed if your bend is not too aesthetically appealing as good glassworking takes many hours of practice.

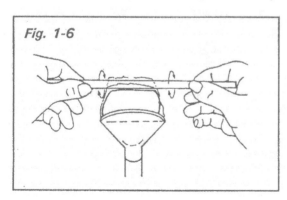

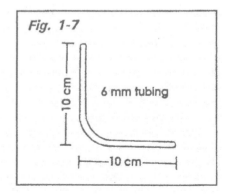

D. Rate of mixing. Mount a 250 mL beaker half full of water on a wire gauze above a Bunsen burner. Heat the water to boiling. Using beaker tongs, pour 50 mL of the hot water into a 150 mL beaker. Add 50 mL of room temperature water to a second 150 mL beaker. Use a dropper bottle of food coloring to add a drop of food coloring to each beaker. Hold the dropper over the lip of each beaker, squeeze out one drop and allow it to fall into the water. Try to add the drop to each beaker in the same way. Do not disturb the beaker in any way but carefully observe the beakers for several minutes and then look at them again in about a half hour.

E. Tearing paper. Try to tear a piece of paper (newspaper is preferable) first vertically and then horizontally. Attempt to make the tears fairly rapidly as opposed to doing it in very small sections with your fingers restricting the direction. Describe and explain your observations.

F. Chemistry reference. This exercise involves the first use of the *Handbook of Chemistry and Physics* in the laboratory portion of this course. Before using the *Handbook*, write down what you think are the three most abundant gases in the atmosphere (not counting water vapor which varies from 0% to 4%). Now look up the atmospheric content (do not change your original answer as you will not lose points for being wrong) in the *Handbook* and record the names of the four most abundant gases and their percentages. [Comment: there is a relationship between this section (F) and a later section (K)].

G. Terminology. Terminology and nomenclature are extremely important in chemistry. An understanding of the language of chemistry makes it much easier to communicate with other chemists and to understand their observations and results. In fact without a working ability with chemical terminology and nomenclature, the transfer of knowledge is close to impossible. This exercise will provide an experience with some of the descriptive terms used routinely by chemists. Early in your chemistry textbook and perhaps in the glossary there should be a discussion of each of the terms used here and in the Prelaboratory problem number 7. For this exercise, find at least one example of each term in your laboratory and describe the example. If appropriate, give its use and location. It is permissible to use observations of the exercises in other parts of this experiment as examples.

H. Solutions. In this procedure, you will apply terminology to some observations on solutions of sodium tetraborate and on the temperature dependence of the solubility of this compound. Add about 200 mL of water to a 400 mL beaker. Place the beaker on a hot plate or on a wire gauze supported above a Bunsen burner and heat the water to boiling. *[Caution: Always use* <u>*beaker*</u> *tongs when manipulating beakers of hot liquids. Do not use crucible tongs for beakers.]* While waiting for the water to boil, add about 0.05 gram of sodium tetraborate [$Na_2B_4O_7 \cdot 10\,H_2O$] to about 5 mL of water in a 18 ×150 mm test tube. Mix the contents of the tube by firmly grasping the test tube between your thumb and forefinger of one hand and striking the bottom of the test tube vigorously and frequently with the forefinger of your other hand. *Never* put a thumb over the mouth of the test tube to avoid spilling when shaking. If the method above does not achieve adequate mixing, insert a cork or rubber stopper into the tube and shake as you hold the stopper down with your thumb. Continue mixing until changes are no longer observable. Does the $Na_2B_4O_7 \cdot 10\,H_2O$ completely dissolve and what terminology can now be applied to the mixture? Add an additional 0.05 g of $Na_2B_4O_7 \cdot 10\,H_2O$ and repeat the mixing and observing process. Now add an additional 2

used up oxygen. Repeat the experiment a number of times until you are confident the results are either reproducible within experimental error or not reproducible within experimental error. In the event that you come to the latter conclusion, try to come up with a new hypothesis to explain your observations. If possible, devise experiments to test your new hypothesis and with the permission of the instructor, perform the experiments.

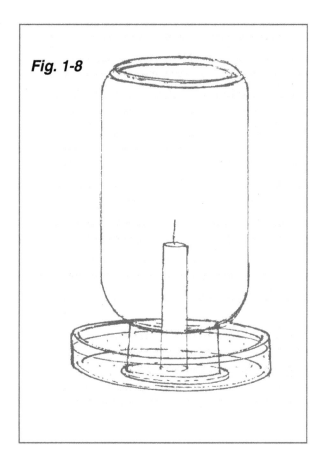

Fig. 1-8

Name_____Date_____Lab Section_____

Prelaboratory Problems - *Experiment 1* - Early Explorations and Terminology
The solutions to the starred problems are in *Appendix 4*.

1.   What color is water?   _____

Problems 2 - 5 describe some observations you have probably made. But have any of the observations stimulated you to the point where you asked a question about them? Try to come up with a question now and suggest an explanation.

2.   Popcorn pops when heated sufficiently.

3.*   Vinegar and oil do not mix.

4.   Your laboratory drawer has Erlenmeyer flasks and beakers that hold similar volumes.

5.*   The necks of volumetric flasks and pipets have very small diameters.

6. Give observations for *Figure 1-9*.

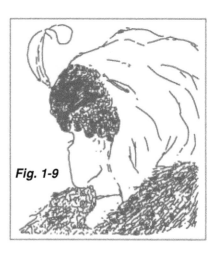

Fig. 1-9

7. Classify the following items a - r using the number codes for the terms below. In some cases, more than one term might be applicable.

    1 substance   4 homogeneous mixture   8 intensive physical property
    2 element   5 heterogeneous mixture   9 extensive physical property
    3 compound   6 saturated solution   10 physical change
                         7 unsaturated solution   11 chemical change

    a.* gold   _____   g. density   _____   m. rusting   _____

    b.* vinegar   _____   h. water   _____   n. iodine   _____

    c.* vinegar &   i. sodium   o. orange
        oil   _____   chloride   _____   juice   _____

    d.* volume   _____   j. evaporation _____   p. vodka.   _____

    e.* melting   k. smog   _____   q. coal
        point   _____   burning   _____

    f.* dilute salt   l. freezing of   r. carbonated
        water   _____   water   _____   soda   _____

8. Compounds are composed of two or more elements. Are the properties of compounds something like an average of the properties of its component elements? Consider for example sodium chloride (NaCl) and iron(III) oxide [commonly called rust (Fe_2O_3)]. Explain your answer.

Name_____Date_____Lab Section_____

Results and Conclusions - *Experiment 1* - Early Explorations and Terminology

A. The meniscus.

    1. Description:

                                                         2. Drawing

    3. Question about the meniscus:

B. The candle flame.

    1. Observations (include comments on states of matter, physical and chemical changes):

    2. What do you think is sustaining the flame (e.g., burning of the wick, the solid wax, the liquid wax or wax vapor)? Explain your answer.

3. Further observations:

   a. beaker partially over burning candle -

   b. stirring rod next to extinguished wick -

   c. burning match approaching extinguished wick -

4. Was your first explanation (question 2) correct or do you want to modify it or suggest a new one? Explain your answer.

C. The Bunsen burner.

1. Draw a picture of the flame. Based on your results with the splint and the gauze, indicate the hottest and coolest regions of the flame.

D. Rate of mixing.

1. Initial observations:

   a. room temperature water

   b. hot water

2. Observations about ¾ hour later:

   a. room temperature water

   b. hot water

3. When two aqueous solutions are introduced into the same container, is stirring needed to achieve a homogeneous system? Explain your answer.

4. How would you stir a solution freshly prepared in a volumetric flask?

E. Tearing paper

1. Describe your observations when you attempted to tear the paper vertically.

2. Describe your observations when you attempted to tear the paper horizontally.

3. Suggest an explanation for any differences observed between vertical and horizontal tearing.

F. Chemistry reference.

Most abundant gases in the atmosphere (excluding water vapor)

Number	Guesstimate	Handbook (edition , page)	%
1	_____	_____	___
2	_____	_____	___
3	_____	_____	___
4	_____	_____	___

Explain why the value for the percentage of carbon dioxide is related to the possibility that the earth could experience a Greenhouse Effect?

G. Terminology (Describe at least one example of each of the following in your laboratory.)

1. substance

2. element

3. compound

4. homogeneous mixture

5. heterogeneous mixture

6. saturated solution

7. unsaturated solution

8. chemical change

9. Shortly after the Chernobyl nuclear reactor accident, some people took potassium iodide tablets to dilute the radioactive iodide in their bodies and diminish its retention in the thyroid gland. Although many experts questioned this practice, little harm was probably caused because of the relatively low toxicity of KI. However, on May 12, 1986, *Newsweek* incorrectly captioned a photo that showed a child apparently receiving KI with "On Alert: Administering iodine to Polish children." Critically evaluate the mistake and possible consequences.

H. Solutions. [Be sure to use appropriate terminology from the section above for all of these questions.]

1. Describe the test tube contents after you have added 0.05 gram of sodium tetraborate decahydrate and stirred..

2. Describe any significant changes after an additional 0.05 gram of $Na_2B_4O_7 \cdot 10\,H_2O$ is added and mixed.

3. How can the sodium tetraborate - water system be distinguished from a compound?

4. Describe your observations when an additional 2 grams of $Na_2B_4O_7 \cdot 10 H_2O$ is added to the solution.

5. What happens to the mixture in *#4* when it is heated?

6. Describe what happens when the solution from *#5* is allowed to cool. Are your observations consistent with your expectations? Explain your answer.

I. Colors.

1. List the colored cations and their colors.

<u>cation</u>	<u>color</u>	<u>cation</u>	<u>color</u>	<u>cation</u>	<u>color</u>
_____	_____	_____	_____	_____	_____
_____	_____	_____	_____	_____	_____

2. Can you make any generalizations about color versus position in the periodic chart?

3. List the colored anions and their colors.

<u>anion</u>	<u>color</u>	<u>anion</u>	<u>color</u>	<u>anion</u>	<u>color</u>
_____	_____	_____	_____	_____	_____
_____	_____	_____	_____		

J. Chemical Reactions.

<u>Reaction</u>   <u>Observations</u>

A

B

C

D

E

K. Mystery flask.

1. Observations upon standing:

2. Observations upon swirling:

3. Suggest an explanation for the change that occurs upon swirling.

4. How could you test your explanation (it might be possible with your instructor's approval to actually perform the test).

L. Classic Burning Candle Experiment.

    1. Trial 1 water level (distance above dish water level)   _____

    2. Volume of water that moved into bottle   _____

    3. Volume of bottle   _____

    4. Percentage of bottle filled by water   _____

    5. Additional trial water levels   _____   _____   _____   _____

    6. Based on the percentage of the bottle filled by the water, is it likely that the water simply displaced used up oxygen? Explain your answer.

    7. Based on the reproducibility of the results, does the hypothesis that the water is displacing used oxygen fit the observations? Explain your answer

    8. If your answer to number 7 was negative, suggest another hypothesis to explain your observations.

    9. Suggest and if possible perform experiments to test your hypothesis in number 8. Describe the experiments and their results. Do the experiments support or refute your new hypothesis?

    10. Some of the *Learning Objectives* of this experiment are listed on the first page of this experiment. Did you achieve the *Learning Objectives*? Explain your answer.

SEPARATION OF MIXTURES

early filtration
apparatus

Learning Objectives

Upon completion of this experiment, students will have experienced:
1. The evaporation of water from salt water.
2. The separation of a solid from a liquid using gravity filtration.
3. Recrystallization and use of vacuum filtration.

Text Topics

Physical properties, separations of mixtures using physical properties, temperature effects on solubility (for correlation to some textbooks, see page ix).

Notes to Students and Instructor

The vanillin recrystallized in this experiment will be saved for **Experiment 3** where its percent recovery and purity will be determined.

Discussion

Imagine yourself by a river in the mountains. You are thirsty but is it safe to drink the water? Probably not because the river is not just water but is a mixture of several substances and probably contains bacteria that can cause intestinal problems. Almost everything that we encounter in nature is a mixture and this adds a challenge to the work of chemists. Analytical chemists may need to know what substances are present (e.g., are pesticides in a water supply?) and this usually involves separation and purification before some type of identification test can be performed. Most physical and chemical tests on mixtures do not give results that can be easily interpreted. The chemist may also need a substance for use as a starting material in a chemical reaction. The presence of impurities may affect or even eliminate the desired reaction. Even chemicals obtained from the stockroom are not absolutely pure with grades of purity generally ranging between 90 and 99.99%. Sometimes small amounts of impurities can be tolerated and in other cases, they must be removed. Would you want as much as 0.1% of a toxic substance in a medicine?

Many separation and purification techniques have been developed. You will use several during this course and three important ones in today's experiment. Try to consider the applicability of each technique as you use it. Can it be used on large samples or only small ones? Will it work to remove large amounts of impurities or only trace constituents? Will it work on any of the three common states of matter or only one? The three techniques you will use today all take advantage of differences in physical properties of the substances being separated. The evaporation of water from salt water to leave behind the desired sodium chloride utilizes the differences in boiling points of water and sodium chloride. The gravity filtration to collect calcium carbonate takes advantage of the very low solubility of calcium carbonate in water and the ability of filter paper to allow passage of a liquid but not a solid. Finally the recrystallization of vanillin relies on the observation that solubility of a solid in a liquid often increases with increasing temperature.

Procedure

A. Evaporation: Determination of the mass percent of sodium chloride in a saturated sodium chloride solution. The amount of sodium chloride dissolved in a saturated solution can be determined by evaporating a weighed amount of a saturated solution to dryness. Dryness is confirmed by repeated heating and weighing cycles until a constant mass is achieved. Decant (be careful not to agitate) about 6 mL of a saturated sodium chloride solution into a 10 mL graduated cylinder. Weigh a clean, dry, evaporating dish to the nearest 0.01 g (preferably 0.001 g) and add the 6 mL of NaCl solution to it. Reweigh the dish and its contents.

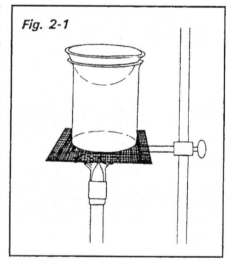

Fig. 2-1

Put a 400 mL beaker about half full of water on a wire gauze above a Bunsen burner. Suspend the evaporating dish in the 400 mL beaker. Boil the water (add water as needed to the beaker to maintain a reasonable level) until the evaporating dish attains apparent dryness (about 20 minutes). Using beaker tongs, remove the beaker and evaporating dish from the flame. Holding it with crucible tongs, place the evaporating dish on a wire gauze and gently flame it for about 3 minutes and allow the dish to cool. Weigh the dish to the at least the nearest 0.01 gram. Again flame the evaporating dish gently for several minutes, cool, and weigh. Repeat the process until successive weighing differences are less than 0.01 g. Calculate the mass percent of NaCl in the saturated solution.

B. Filtration: Collection of calcium carbonate. The addition of aqueous calcium chloride to aqueous sodium carbonate results in a double replacement reaction or an exchange of the positive and negative partners of two ionic compounds.

$$Na_2CO_3(aq) + CaCl_2(aq) = 2NaCl(aq) + CaCO_3(s)$$

As calcium carbonate is not soluble in water, it precipitates out of the solution. The solid calcium carbonate can be separated from the solution by gravity filtration.

Pour about 10 mL of 1.0 M sodium carbonate solution into your graduated cylinder and transfer this solution to a 150 mL beaker. Add 10 mL of 1.0 M calcium chloride solution to the beaker, stir, and report your observations. Save for the filtration.

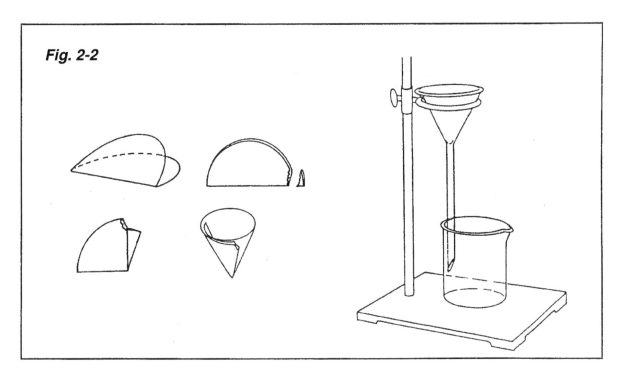

Fig. 2-2

Select a piece of filter paper that is the appropriate size for your long stem funnel. After being folded and opened into a cone, it should fit slightly below the glass rim of the funnel. For the most common size funnel, this paper will have a 12.5 cm diameter. Fold a piece of filter paper in half. Tear off about a half centimeter piece from one corner then fold it into quarters. Open up one pocket of the filter paper so that it forms the shape of a complete cone. Put it into your funnel and wet it thoroughly with deionized water from your wash bottle so that it adheres uniformly and seals to the inside wall of the funnel. Swirl the reaction mixture and transfer part of it to the filter. Make sure the liquid does not get closer than 0.5 cm to the top edge of the filter paper. Continue adding the mixture until all of it has been added to the funnel. With a wash bottle, squirt some water into the beaker and transfer this wash water to the funnel. Repeat this process two more times. Allow the funnel to drain. When the dripping has virtually stopped, scrape the precipitate onto a watch glass with a stirring rod. Using a medicine dropper, rapidly add about 10 drops of 6 M HCl to the precipitate. Describe your observations.

Whenever a chemical synthesis is attempted (in this case calcium carbonate), it is necessary to verify that the intended product has been isolated. The addition of an acid to a carbonate yields carbon dioxide gas. The observation that a gas evolves provides some evidence but certainly not proof that a carbonate has been synthesized.

Try adding a few drops of 6 M HCl to a small piece of egg shell. Report your observations and conclusions concerning the composition of the egg shell.

C. Recrystallization: Purification of vanillin. The solubility of many solids increases dramatically as the solvent temperature increases. A barely saturated solution of the solid in a hot solvent is prepared and allowed to cool. The solubility decreases as the temperature drops and causes recrystallization to occur. The crystals are collected by vacuum filtration hopefully in a purer condition than before they were dissolved in the solvent. Insoluble impurities are removed by filtration of the hot saturated solution and soluble impurities stay dissolved in the solvent and do not crystallize upon cooling. These impurities pass through the final cold filtration.

In the following recrystallization of vanillin, recognize that the difficult part of the experiment has already been done for you. For a recrystallization, a solvent must first be found which will dissolve the vanillin when hot but not when cold. Appropriate amounts must also be chosen. Water turns out to be a good solvent for the recrystallization of vanillin and reasonable amounts have been determined by experimentation and reported to you. *Be sure to save the vanillin that you purify today for **Experiment 3** where you will determine the percent recovery from the recrystallization and the success of the attempted purification.*

Weigh into a 125 or 250 mL Erlenmeyer flask about 2 g of vanillin to the balance limit. Add about 60 mL of deionized water to the flask and stir vigorously. Using a Bunsen burner, heat the solution just to the boiling point and stir until all the solid dissolves. Allow the solution to cool on your desk for several minutes and then put the flask into an ice bath.

Crystallization should occur on its own but occasionally supersaturation occurs and crystallization needs a little assistance. If this happens, try rubbing the inside of the flask beneath the liquid line with a glass rod hard enough to make a grinding sound. If this does not work, seeding with a small crystal of impure vanillin or better yet, a crystal of another student's recrystallized vanillin should initiate the process. After crystallization is complete and the flask has been cooled to about 5°C, isolate the vanillin using vacuum filtration. Obtain a Buchner funnel and filter flask and assemble them as in *Figure 2-3*. Select a piece of filter paper that has been precut to just fit in the bottom of the Buchner funnel.

Connect the filter flask to an aspirator (Note: It is good lab practice to include a trap between the aspirator and the filter flask as water sometimes backs up from the aspirator into the filter flask. However, in this case you are interested in collecting the precipitate only and the filtrate will be discarded. If the filtrate is needed, be sure to use a trap to prevent contamination.) and wet the paper in the filter with deionized water from a wash bottle. Turn the aspirator on full and transfer the contents of the Erlenmeyer to the Buchner funnel. Rinse the Erlenmeyer flask out once or twice with 5 mL of ice-cooled water and use this water to wash the crystals in the funnel. Weigh a piece of filter paper. Empty the crystals onto the weighed filter paper and place them in your desk for drying, being sure they cannot spill. You will weigh the product and check its purity next week.

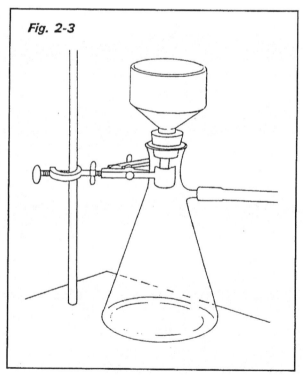

Fig. 2-3

Name_____Date_____Lab Section_____

Prelaboratory Problems - *Experiment 2* - **Separation of Mixtures**
The solutions to the starred problems are in *Appendix 4*.

1.* 6.7 mL of a potassium chloride solution was added to a 54.730 g evaporating dish. The combination weighed 61.945 g. After evaporation the dish and contents weighed 55.428 g.

    a. What was the mass percent of potassium chloride in the solution?   _____

    b. If the actual mass percent of potassium in the above solution was 10.00%, what was the percentage error of the above measurement?

                              _____

    c. Why was evaporation used to determine the mass percentage of potassium chloride in the solution rather than filtration or recrystallization? Explain your answer.

    d. Compare the mass percent calculated in # 1-c above to the value for a saturated solution in *Appendix 3*. Was the solution prepared above saturated? Explain your answer.

2. 8.5 mL of a sample of sea water solution was added to a 44.317 g evaporating dish. The combination weighed 52.987 g. After evaporation the dish and contents weighed 44.599 g.

    a. What was the mass percent of dissolved solids in the sea water?

                              _____

b. The actual sodium chloride content in the sea water was 2.69%. If it had been assumed that the dissolved solid(s) consisted only of sodium chloride, what percentage error would have resulted? [Caution: the answer is not 0.56%]? The numbers included here are for a typical sea water sample. In addition to NaCl, typical sea water contains about 0.56% by mass of compounds (primarily chlorides) of magnesium, calcium and potassium.

_____

c. Could the dissolved solids have been isolated using either filtration or recrystallization? Explain your answer.

3. Aspirin (acetyl salicylic acid) can be synthesized by reacting acetic anhydride with salicylic acid. Assume the reaction was run and 1.75 grams of a solid product was obtained. Recrystallization of the 1.75 g mixture yielded 1.50 g of aspirin.

a. What was the percentage recovery of aspirin from the recrystallization?

_____

b. Why was recrystallization used for the purification of aspirin rather than filtration or evaporation? Explain your answer.

4. The reaction of aqueous solutions of barium chloride and sodium sulfate results in the formation of a precipitate of barium sulfate. Sodium chloride is also formed but is soluble in water. Why would you use filtration to isolate the barium sulfate rather than evaporation or recrystallization? Explain your answer.

$$BaCl_2(aq) + Na_2SO_4(aq) = BaSO_4(s) + 2\,NaCl(aq)$$

Name_____Date_____Lab Section_____

Results and Discussion - *Experiment 2* - Separation of Mixtures

A. **Evaporation: Determination of the mass percent of sodium chloride in a saturated sodium chloride solution.**

   1. Mass of evaporating dish _____

   2. Mass of dish and sodium chloride solution _____

   3. Mass of dish and sodium chloride (1st heating) _____

   4. Mass of dish and sodium chloride (2nd heating) _____

   5. Mass of dish and sodium chloride (3rd heating if necessary) _____

   6. Mass of saturated sodium chloride solution _____

   7. Mass of sodium chloride _____

   8. Mass percent of sodium chloride in saturated solution _____

   9. Calculate the percentage deviation between your value and an accepted literature value of 26.4%. _____

   10. Is sea water close to being a saturated sodium chloride solution? Explain your answer [Hint: See *Prelaboratory Problem* #2-b in this experiment.]. _____

   11. How could you tell that the original salt solution was saturated?

B. Filtration: Collection of calcium carbonate.

1. What did you observe when you mixed solutions of sodium carbonate and calcium chloride?   _____

2. What did you observe when you added HCl to the product of your reaction?   _____

3. What conclusion did you draw from your observations in #2?

4. What did you observe when you added HCl to a piece of egg shell?   _____

5. What conclusion did you come to about the egg shell from your observations in #4?

6. Buildings and statues contain significant percentages of carbonates. Based on your observations in #2 and #4, what effects could acid rain have on these structures?

C. Recrystallization: Purification of vanillin.

1. Mass of crude vanillin (also enter on page 41)   _____

2. Mass of paper used for storing vanillin (also enter on page 41)   _____

3. Why is the vanillin solution cooled in an ice bath before vacuum filtration?

4. What additional step could be added to this procedure to remove impurities insoluble in the solvent?   _____

5. Some of the *Learning Objectives* of this experiment are listed on the first page of this experiment. Did you achieve the *Learning Objectives*? Explain your answer.

Name_____Date_____Lab Section_____

Postlaboratory Problems - *Experiment 2* - **Separation of Mixtures**
(Note: It might be useful to refer to the solubility chart in *Appendix 3* for some of these questions.)

A. Evaporation: Determination of the mass percent of sodium chloride in a saturated sodium chloride solution.

   1.   What criteria do you think were used is the selection of this system?

       a.   Why was water chosen for the solvent?

       b.   Why was sodium chloride chosen for the solute?

       c.   Suggest reasons why the following were not chosen for the solute:

           calcium carbonate ($CaCO_3$)

           sodium cyanide (NaCN)

           gold chloride ($AuCl_3$)

           hydrogen chloride (HCl)

   2.   For the evaporation of NaCl, why is the heat-cool-weigh cycle repeated until constant mass is attained?

   3.   Would evaporation be a very useful separation technique for solutions that contain more than one solute? Explain your answer.

B. Filtration: Collection of calcium carbonate.

Why was gravity filtration used instead of evaporation to isolate the calcium carbonate (consider question *A-3* above)?

C. Recrystallization: Purification of vanillin.

1.   What criteria do you think were used to select the solute and solvent for this experiment?

2.   a.   Suggest any limitations to the use of recrystallization as a purification method for a solid.

      b.   Suggest reasons why recrystallization from water would probably not be a suitable procedure for purifying the following substances:

            sodium chloride (NaCl) (Hint: Look up its solubility and also the dependence of the solubility on temperature in your textbook.)

            calcium carbonate ($CaCO_3$)

            ethanol (C_2H_6O)

3.   Gravity and vacuum filtration separate insoluble solids from a liquid phase. The choice depends on conditions. Suggest criteria you would apply to choose between them.

4.   What happens to the salt concentration in a saturated solution if the water is allowed to evaporate (assume constant temperature is maintained)? Explain your answer.

5.   Suggest any ways you can think of to improve any part(s) of this experiment.

MEASUREMENTS AND IDENTIFICATION TECHNIQUES

Learning Objectives

Upon completion of this experiment, students will have experienced:
1. The determination of the percent recovery and purity of recrystallized vanillin (from **Experiment 2**).
2. The determination of melting points using the capillary technique and the effects of impurities on melting points.
3. The determination of the density of a solid using two methods.

Text Topics

Significant figures, melting points, density (for correlation to some texts, see p. ix).

Notes to Students and Instructor

With proper preparation, this experiment and part of the next one can be performed in one laboratory period.

Discussion

The importance of careful and complete descriptive observations cannot be overstated. Often, however, it is desirable to seek quantitative relationships between variables. To accomplish this, we need to perform measurements using a consistent set of units. We know that the volume of a gas will increase as the temperature is increased but can we predict how much it will increase? By measuring the volume of a gas as a function of temperature, it is possible to develop an empirical relationship between volume and temperature. Application of the kinetic theory yields the same equation providing support for the validity of the theory.

For units, scientists have joined most of the rest of the world in adopting the convenient and rational metric system. Prefixes relate different length, mass and volume systems by powers of ten (rather than factors of 4, 12, 16, 36 or 5280). Volume is defined in terms of distance cubed (1 L = 1 dm^3 therefore 1 mL = 1 cm^3) instead of independently (how many gallons in 1 ft^3?). The mass scale has been established so that at 3.98°C, water has a density of exactly 1 g/cm^3 or 1 g/mL (What is the density of water in lbs/ft^3 or lbs/gal?). The metric temperature scale is in Celsius degrees with the freezing and boiling points of water logically defined as 0°C and 100°C respectively.

This experiment will focus on techniques of reading, recording, and utilizing measurements. **One of the most important rules to remember is that you should estimate and record 1 digit beyond the last set of graduations on your measuring instrument** (this rule doesn't apply to many of the new high tech instruments that have digital readout although sometimes fluctuation in the last digit is observed and you then do estimate the most probable value of that digit). The estimated digit does have significance and is therefore counted as a *significant figure*. In *Figure 3-1*, the reading should be recorded as 21.7 mL and not 22 mL. The bottom of the meniscus (see *Experiment 1*) is obviously below 22.0 mL and above 21.5 mL. To write down 22 mL would be communicating that the value is between 21 and 23 mL. But it is clear that the reading provides more information than this. The value 21.7 mL communicates to the reader that the value is probably between 21.6 and 21.8 mL. A second rule is that *when the estimated digit is a zero* (this should happen about 1

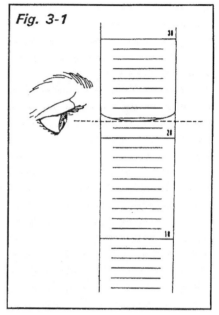

out of every 10 readings), *the zero must be recorded*. The thermometer below reads 23.0°C. 23°C is an inadequate recording of the temperature as it states that the reading is between 22 and 24°C but observation indicates that it is between 22.9 and 23.1°C

Be especially careful with zeros when a decimal is not showing. If you say you are driving 90 km/hr, do you mean between 89 and 91 or between 80 and 100 (the former should be written 9.0×10^1 km/hr and the latter either 90 km/hr or preferably 9×10^1 km/hr). For more information on measurements, significant figures and rounding off, refer to your textbook.

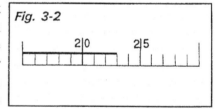

Intensive Physical Properties. Whether dealing with an unknown chemical extracted from a plant or the product of a chemical synthesis, chemical identification can often pose a significant challenge to the chemist. For previously characterized compounds, a comparison of properties of the unknown with those of knowns will usually make an identification possible. To be useful for identification purposes, a property must not depend on the amount of substance. Extensive properties such as mass and volume do depend on the amount of substance and are not useful for identification purposes. However, intensive properties such as melting points and densities do not depend on the amount of material and are and very useful for identification purposes. Melting points of substances are significantly depressed by many additives or impurities. Thus, in addition to being useful for identification purposes, melting points are useful in determining purity.

The density (mass/volume) of a substance is also an intensive property. 1.00 mL of mercury has a mass of 13.6 grams and a density of 13.6 g/mL. 10.0 mL of mercury has a mass of 136 grams and a density of 13.6 g/mL. Although density does require two measurements, mass and volume, both are relatively easy to measure. Comprehensive tables of densities and melting points have been compiled and both are commonly used for identification purposes.

Procedure

A. Percent recovery. Determine the percent recovery of vanillin by weighing the vanillin obtained from the recrystallization in *Experiment 2*, dividing the amount by the original amount of crude vanillin and then multiplying by 100%. When you are finished with the vanillin, in *Parts A and B,* return your recrystallized vanillin as the vanillin can be used again in *Experiment 2*.

B. Melting points. The melting point of a pure substance can be measured quickly using the capillary method (described later). The method is accurate to within a few tenths of a degree and requires only a small amount of sample. For identification purposes, the determination of the melting point usually narrows down the number of possible compounds to two or three. When a contaminated compound is melted, we should notice two distinguishing features. First, as with ice water contaminated by salt, the melting point is lowered by additives. Second, the melting process occurs over more than a few tenths of a degree range and is more properly called a melting range than a melting point. **It is very important that the total range be reported; that is the temperature at which the first minute amount of liquid appears to the temperature at which the sample is totally liquid.** The extent of depression and broadening of the melting range serves as a useful measure of the purity of a sample. Very roughly each 1% of impurity (up to about 10%) will depress the high value of the range about 1° below the melting point of the pure compound. Utilizing the melting point depression phenomenon, it is even possible to distinguish between two possible compounds with the same melting points if labeled samples of the two are available (See *Prelaboratory Problem 5*).

The capillary technique is illustrated in *Figures 3-3* and *3-4*. Select a thermometer that covers the range -10°C to 110°C. Capillary tubes are very convenient sample holders as they are inexpensive and hold very small amounts of sample that can be easily observed during the melting process. Fill the capillary tube by pressing the open end onto the powdered sample until there is about a 0.5-1 cm length of sample in the tube. Now drop the capillary tube, sealed end down, through a 1 meter piece of 6 mm glass tubing that is being held on a hard surface. The impact of the capillary with the hard surface seldom results in breaking and causes the sample to drop to the bottom of the tube. Repeat the dropping procedure until the sample is packed in the bottom of the tube. Attach the capillary tube with a rubber ring (cut off a piece of rubber hose) to a thermometer with the sample even with the mercury bulb of the thermometer. Place the thermometer in a 250 mL beaker half full of water mounted above a Bunsen burner. Support the thermometer using a *split* rubber stopper supported by a clamp on a ring stand. Gently heat the water with **continual** stirring and observe the sample. As you approach the melting range, slow the heating rate to around 2°C/min. Heating the sample too rapidly near its melting range will result in large errors. At the first indication of sample melting, record the temperature to the nearest 0.1°C. Continue to slowly heat until the sample has totally liquified and record the high end of the melting range.

Using the technique described above, determine the melting ranges of the three samples below. [Hint: The melting ranges should occur between 60°C and 85°C. As the melting range is approached, the heating rate should be kept as slow as possible.] For the mixed sample, add approximately equal amounts of each compound to a mortar and grind them together with a pestle before inserting into a capillary tube. Don't forget to recycle your vanillin.

a. Impure vanillin from **Experiment 2.**
b. Recrystallized vanillin from **Experiment 2.**
c. 50% recrystallized vanillin + 50% phenyl carbonate

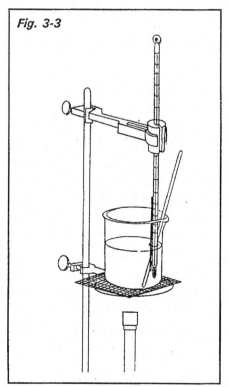

Fig. 3-3

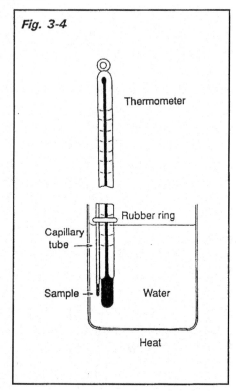

Fig. 3-4

C. Density. The density, or mass/volume, of a metal cylinder will be calculated twice using two different methods to determine its volume. Then you will use the density to attempt to identify the metal. First use your balance to determine the mass of the metal cylinder to the limits of the balance (probably either 0.01 g or 0.001 g.).

1. Volume from linear measurements: For regularly shaped objects such as a cylinder, it is usually possible to measure the dimensions of the object and use a formula to calculate the volume of the object. The volume of a cylinder is calculated by multiplying π times the square of its radius times its length ($V = \pi r^2 L$). Using a metric ruler or preferably vernier calipers, measure the diameter and length of the cylinder and calculate its volume and density.

2. Volume from water displacement: A more general method for volume determination that will work with regular and irregular shaped objects is the method of water displacement. The water level in a graduated cylinder is recorded, an object submerged in the water and the new water level read. The difference in water levels is the volume of the object. Obtain an appropriately sized graduated cylinder for your metal cylinder and fill it about half full with water. Read the water level, tilt the graduated cylinder and slide the metal cylinder gently into the water being sure that it is completely submerged. Read the resulting water level and calculate the volume and density of the object.

3. Assume the metal cylinder is one of the following: aluminum, copper, iron or lead. Look up the density of each metal and determine the composition of your cylinder.

Name_____Date_____Lab Section_____

Prelaboratory Problems - *Experiment 3* - Measurement and Identification
The solutions to the starred problems are in *Appendix 4*.

1. Math review problems

    a.* How many significant figures are in each of the following numbers?

    405.0 _____   0.0789 _____   2.040 _____   360 _____ 3.00×10^{10} _____

    b. Express each of the following with three significant figures.

    0.002537 _____   12345000 _____   0.07966 _____   620.2 _____

    c. Perform the following operations: 4.5×10^3 cm + 1.6×10^2 cm = _____

    $(1.5 \times 10^{-3}$ mole$)\dfrac{(6.022 \times 10^{23} \text{ molecules})}{1 \text{ mole}}$ = _____ $\dfrac{1.80 \times 10^{-6} \text{ g}}{2.00 \times 10^{-3} \text{ mL}}$ = _____

2. List at least four distinct advantages of the metric system over "our" measurement system.

3. a.* Salt is often spread on icy roads in the winter. What is its function and how does it work?

    b. Due to the use of salt on roads, two towns in Massachusetts were having problems with high salt content in ground water supplies. One town chose not to use salt one winter and the automobile accident rate actually went down. Suggest a reason for this unexpected result and comment on the validity of long range conclusions from this study.

    c. When preparing home-made ice cream, salt is added to the ice-water mixture. What is its function and why does it work?

    d. Antifreeze (commonly ethylene glycol or propylene glycol) is usually mixed with water in the radiator of a car. What is its function and how does it work?

4.*   A 2.5 g sample of naphthalene (melting range 73.4-77.1°C) is recrystallized and 1.8 grams of purified naphthalene (melting range 80.5-80.6°C) are recovered.

    a.   What is the percent recovery?   _____

    b.   Comment on the purity of the original naphthalene sample.

    c.   Comment on the success of the recrystallization.

5.   Cinnamic acid and urea melt at 133°C. The melting point of an unknown is found to be 133°C. What experiments using melting range determinations could be done to determine if the unknown is cinnamic acid or urea?

6.*   A 15.00 g metal sphere was found to have a diameter of 1.85 cm. The volume of a sphere is $V = (4/3)\pi r^3$. Calculate the density of the sphere and assuming that the sphere is made out of one of the elements, aluminum, chromium, iron, lead, titanium or zinc, determine its composition.

7.   A 55.81 gram irregular object made out of one of the metals in #6 raises the water level in a graduated cylinder from the 17.6 mL level to the 24.7 mL level. What is the density and identity of the metal?

Name_____Date_____Lab Section_____

Results and Discussion - *Experiment 3* - Measurement and Identification

A. Percent Recovery

1. Mass of weighed filter paper   _____

2. Mass of weighed filter paper plus recrystallized vanillin   _____

3. Mass of recrystallized vanillin   _____

4. Mass of impure vanillin (from last week)   _____

5. Percent recovery   _____

6. Suggest how you could have improved your techniques to increase your percent recovery.

B. Melting Point Determinations

1. Melting range of impure vanillin   _____

2. Melting range of recrystallized vanillin   _____

3. Melting range of 50% recrystallized vanillin + 50% phenyl carbonate   _____

4. *Handbook of Chemistry and Physics* value for the melting range of vanillin   _____

   and for phenyl carbonate   _____
   (edition _____ pages _____)

5. Did your recrystallization significantly purify the vanillin? Explain your answer.

6. How can rapid heating while using the capillary melting point technique give erroneous results?

C. Density

1. Linear measurement method

   a. Identification number of metal cylinder   _____

   b. Mass of metal cylinder   _____

   c. Length of metal cylinder   _____

   d. Diameter of metal cylinder   _____

   e. Radius of metal cylinder   _____

   f. Volume of metal cylinder   _____

   g. Density of metal cylinder   _____

2. Water displacement method (cylinder i.d. number and mass same as above)

   a. Initial volume of water in graduated cylinder   _____

   b. Final volume of water in graduated cylinder   _____

   c. Volume of metal cylinder   _____

   d. Density of metal cylinder   _____

3. Identity of metal

   Handbook of Chemistry and Physics values for the density of:

   a. aluminum   _____

   b. copper   _____

   c. iron   _____

   d. lead   _____

   e. Identity of metal   _____

4. For a regular shaped object such as the metal cylinder used in this experiment, which of the two methods do you think is preferable for a density determination. Give reasons for your preference.

5. Some of the *Learning Objectives* of this experiment are listed on the first page of this experiment. Did you achieve the *Learning Objectives*? Explain your answer.

Name_____Date_____Lab Section_____

Postlaboratory Problems - *Experiment 3* - **Measurement and Identification**

1. Why is it important to determine the percent recovery for chemical processes? In addition to considering its importance in the chemical laboratory, consider its importance to a chemical company.

2. Why is it important to determine the melting ranges of the impure and recrystallized samples of vanillin?

3. Melting ranges are helpful for identification purposes and determining purity. Would the melting range of a new (never before reported) compound be worth determining and if so, why?

4. What properties must a solid have for the water displacement method to be useful?

5. For each of the following solids, describe how you would determine its density.

   a.   a ball bearing

   b.   10 grams of granular zinc

   c.   10 grams of granular sodium chloride

   d.   an irregular shaped piece of maple (about 10 grams)

   e.   a lump of sodium (about 10 grams)

6. Another way of determining the volume of solid makes use of the fact that the difference in the mass of an object determined directly and suspended in water is the mass of the water displaced by the object. Division of this mass by the density of water gives the volume of the water displaced and therefore the volume of the object. Would this method have any advantages over the water displacement method used in this experiment?

7. Suggest further tests for distinguishing two metals that have densities within the experimental errors of each other.

8. Suggest any ways you can think of to improve any part(s) of this experiment.

4

DENSITY, ACCURACY, PRECISION AND GRAPHING

Learning Objectives

Upon completion of this experiment, students will have experienced:
1. The determination of the density of water and a saline solution.
2. A comparison of the accuracy and precision of a graduated cylinder and a pipet.
3. Graphing.

Text Topics

Significant figures, density determinations, accuracy and precision (see page ix).

Notes to Students and Instructor

With proper preparation, it should be possible to perform this experiment and the next one or parts of the previous one in one laboratory period.

Discussion

In the previous experiment, the density of a solid was determined using two different techniques. For a short review of the concept of density, reread the *Discussion* for **Experiment 3**. Today's experiment will involve the determination of densities of liquids, a comparison of the accuracy and precision of a graduated cylinder and pipet and application of proper graphing techniques to density problems.

Accuracy and Precision. The layperson might not distinguish between accuracy and precision, but to a scientist, they have different meanings. Accuracy is a measure of how close an experimental value is to the actual value. If you measure the circumference of a circle as 25.00 cm and the diameter as 8.000 cm, the value of π that results is 25.00/8.000 = 3.125. The value 3.125 has a percentage error of:

$$\left(\frac{3.1416 - 3.125}{3.1416} \right)(100\%) \ = \ 0.53\%.$$

The 0.53% disparity is a measure of the (in)accuracy of the result.

Precision is the reproducibility of the measurement or how closely the measurements agree with each other. Precision is often indicated by the number of significant figures. A measurement of 25.0 cm should be more precise than a measurement of 25 cm as repeated measurements for the former should fall between 24.9 cm and 25.1 cm whereas measurements for the latter should fall between 24 cm and 26 cm. The values between 24.9 cm and 25.1 cm are clearly closer together.

Although the most accurate values are usually the most precise and vice versa, there are exceptions. Very imprecise measurements might by coincidence average out to yield a very accurate value. Or, an incorrectly calibrated device might yield precise but inaccurate measurements.

Graphing. It is very common for scientific experiments to result in tables full of data. While it is sometimes possible to come to meaningful conclusions from tables, it often easier to discern relationships between variables visually using appropriate graphs. A graph shows how one variable changes as another is varied. A graph should be designed to be easily read and interpreted. The guidelines below should help you prepare readable graphs.

1. Select **logical scales** that utilize as much of the graph paper as possible. For many graphs, the two axes will have different scales. Each division should represent **1, 2, 2.5 or 5 units** or some power of ten times one of these units. Avoid the use of 3 or 7 units/division or another number that makes it difficult to locate points on the graph. Be sure the scales are **linear** unless you are doing a log or another function type plot. Unless extrapolating, the graph should cover only the range of measurements on each axis. It is **not** necessary for the point 0, 0 to be on the graph.

2. Label the axes and indicate units used.

3. Locate the points and put dots at the proper locations. **Circle** the dots.

4. If the points appear to fall on a straight line, use a **straight edge** to draw the line that best fits (averages the deviations) the data. Do not sketch straight lines and do not connect the dots with straight line segments. If the points seem to fall on a smooth curve, draw the best curve possible through the data.

Procedure

A. Density of water. The density of three different volumes of water measured with a graduated cylinder will be determined and the mass of the water plotted against its volume.

1. Weigh an empty, **dry** 50 mL graduated cylinder to your balance limits (0.01 g or 0.001 g).

2. Add 10.0 mL of water to the cylinder. Remember, the <u>very</u> bottom of the meniscus should just be touching the 10.0 mL line. Add water up to about the 9 mL mark and use a dropper to reach the 10.0 mL mark.

3. Weigh the cylinder + 10.0 mL of water. You can now calculate the density of the water.

4. Add water up to the 30.0 mL mark and weigh.

5. Add water up to the 50.0 mL mark and weigh.

6. Calculate the densities of the three **total** volumes.

7. As a beginning exercise in graphing, plot the masses of the water on the vertical scale versus the volumes of the water on the horizontal scale.

    B. Accuracy and precision. Triplicate determinations of the density of water will be made on 10 mL water samples measured with a graduated cylinder and also with a 10 mL volumetric pipet. Each 10 mL water sample will be weighed and the density calculated. Average densities and average deviations for each measuring device will be calculated and the accuracy and precision of the graduated cylinder and pipet will be compared.

    Weigh a 150 mL beaker to the balance limits. Now add 10.0 mL of deionized water to your graduated cylinder. Transfer the 10.0 mL of water to the beaker and weigh the beaker accurately again. Add 10.0 mL more of water from the graduated cylinder to the beaker and weigh again. Repeat this process a third time. Calculate the mass and density of **each** 10.0 mL portion.

    Using a pipet bulb, draw deionized water (not from the beaker you just weighed) into a 10 mL volumetric pipet until the water reaches the lower part of the pipet bulge (*Figure 4-1*). Remove the bulb and quickly replace it with your finger. Tip the pipet to a horizontal position and roll the water around being sure to wet all the glass inside the pipet. Drain the pipet out the top. Repeat this rinsing process two more times. Now draw water into the pipet until it is a few centimeters above the fill line in the upper neck. Replace the bulb with your finger and wipe off the outside of the pipet with a towel. Slowly decrease your finger pressure on the pipet opening until the water starts dripping out the tip. Carefully control the dripping until the meniscus just touches the fill line (*Figure 4-2*). Touch the tip to the inside of a glass container to remove the drop or partial drop hanging from the tip. Being sure there are no air bubbles in the tip and the meniscus is still set correctly, drain the pipet into the preweighed beaker allowing the water to drain on its own. Do not use pressure to blow it out. Touch the pipet tip to the inside of the beaker as it completes its draining and hold it there for about 20 seconds after draining is complete. Do not blow out the last half drop as the pipet is calibrated to deliver 10.00 mL from the fill line to the last half drop. Weigh the beaker again and then pipet 10.00 mL more water into it. Repeat this process one more time. Calculate the mass and density of each 10.00 mL portion of water.

    Average the three trials for the graduated cylinder and then the three trials for the pipet. For the graduated cylinder, determine the **absolute** value of the difference between each separate graduated cylinder density measurement and the average value. These three values are the deviations of each measurement from the average. Now average the three deviations to arrive at the average deviation. As you should be able to surmise, the average deviation is a measure of the precision of the measurement. Mathematically the average deviation is not as significant as the standard deviation. While it is not difficult to calculate standard deviations, we have chosen to use average deviations here to simplify this treatment. Find average deviations for the pipet measurements in the same way you found them for the graduated cylinder.

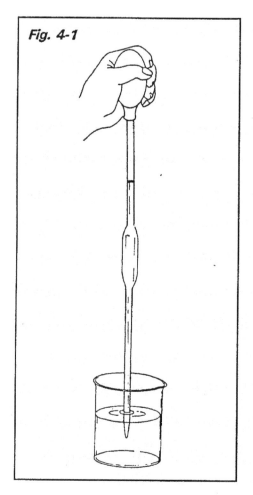

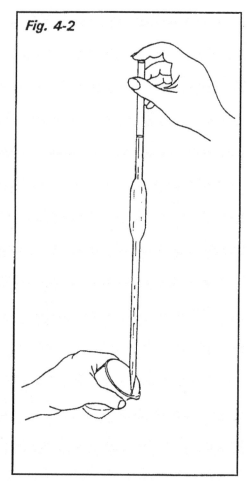

C. Density of a sodium chloride solution. Obtain a salt solution of unknown mass percent salt from your instructor. Rinse a 10.00 mL pipet three times with the unknown solution and then transfer 10.00 mL of the unknown to a preweighed beaker. Weigh the beaker again and calculate the density of the unknown. Use the data in the ***Results and Discussion*** section to plot the density of sodium chloride solutions versus the mass percent of sodium chloride. Use the graph and your experimental density to determine the mass percent of sodium chloride in your unknown. Note that the densities presented of the salt solutions were measured at 20°C. Although densities are temperature dependent, the values are accurate to three significant figures after the decimal between 18 and 24°C. If your solution temperature is not in this range, there will be a slight error.

D. Relative density of liquid and solid phases of a substance. Pour about 5 mL of acetophenone into a 13 x 100 mm test tube. Put the test tube in an ice bath until the acetophenone is frozen solid. Warm the test tube with your hand or a room temperature water bath just sufficiently to be able to slide the frozen acetophenone into an 18 x 150 mm test tube. Add about 3 mL of liquid acetophenone, shake, observe and record your observations and measure the temperature of the system. Return the acetophenone to the used acetophenone bottle.

Add some ice to water and shake and observe (if all the ice melts during shaking, add some more so that the test tube has both liquid and solid water).

Name_____Date_____Lab Section_____

Prelaboratory Problems - *Experiment 4* - **Density, Accuracy, Precision and Graphing**   The solutions to the starred problems are in *Appendix 4*.

1. The mass of a 45.750 g piece of copper is measured three times on two different balances with the following results:

Trial	Balance 1 (grams)	Balance 2 (grams)
1	45.747	45.76
2	45.745	45.77
3	45.748	45.74

   a. Calculate the average deviation for each set of measurements on each balance.

                                                      balance 1*   _____

                                                      balance 2   _____

   b. Which balance is more precise? Explain your answer.

   c. Which balance is more accurate? Explain your answer.

2. 25.00 mL of heavy water (D_2O where D is a hydrogen with a neutron in its nucleus) at 20°C was pipetted into a 37.234 g beaker. The final mass of the beaker was 64.859 g.

   a.* What is the density of heavy water at 20°C?   _____

   b.   The density of normal water (the hydrogens do not have neutrons) at 20°C is 0.9982 g/mL. Calculate the density you would expect for heavy water by assuming that deuterium (^2H or ^2D) is the same size as normal hydrogen (^1H) when it is part of the water.

                                                                        _____

   c.   Based on your answer to (b), was the assumption in (b) justified?
        Explain your answer.   _____

3. 15.00 mL of radiator liquid (water + ethylene glycol) from a car has a mass of 15.69 g.

    a. Calculate the density of the radiator liquid.   _____

    b. Based on the calculation above, is the density of ethylene glycol greater
        or less than that of water? Explain your answer.   _____

    c. Use the *Handbook of Chemistry and Physics* to determine the
        mass percent of ethylene glycol in the mixture and the freezing   _____
        temperature of this antifreeze mixture.

                                                                                   _____

Name_____Date_____Lab Section_____

Results and Discussion - *Experiment 4* - **Density, Accuracy, Precision and Graphing**

A. Density of water

	10.0 mL	30.0 mL	50.0 mL
1. Mass of graduated cylinder + water	_____	_____	_____
2. Mass of empty graduated cylinder	_____	_____	_____
3. Mass of water	_____	_____	_____
4. Density of 10.0 mL sample of water	_____		
5. Density of 30.0 mL sample of water		_____	
6. Density of 50.0 mL sample of water			_____

7. Graph mass (not density) on the vertical axis vs volume on the horizontal axis below:

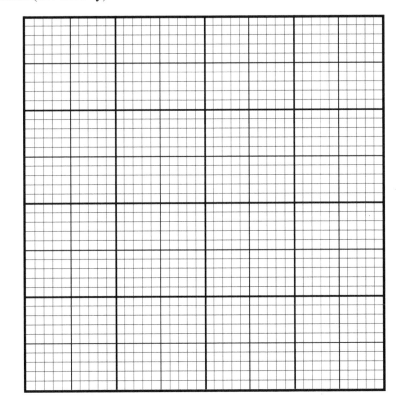

8. The equation for density d = m/v can be rearranged to m = dv.
    What is the meaning and value of the slope of the line?

                                                        slope =   _____

B. Accuracy and Precision

	Graduated Cylinder	Pipet
1. Mass of beaker	_____	_____
2. After first addition	_____	_____
3. After second addition	_____	_____
4. After third addition	_____	_____
5. Mass of **first 10 mL** of water	_____	_____
6. Mass of **second 10 mL** of water	_____	_____
7. Mass of **third 10 mL** of water	_____	_____
8. Temperature of water in beaker	_____	_____
9. Density of water		
a. Trial 1	_____	_____
b. Trial 2	_____	_____
c. Trial 3	_____	_____
10. Average density	=========	=========
11. Deviations from average		
a. Deviation of trial 1	_____	_____
b. Deviation of trial 2	_____	_____
c. Deviation of trial 3	_____	_____
12. Average deviation	=========	=========
13. *Handbook of Chemistry and Physics* value for the density of water at the temperature of your measurement	_____	_____
14. Percentage error of your average density measurement	=========	=========

15. Which volume measuring device was more accurate?
    Explain your answer.   _____

16. Which volume measuring device was more precise?
    Explain your answer.   _____

C. Density of a salt solution.

1. Unknown number   _____

2. Mass of beaker   _____

3. Mass of beaker + 10.00 mL of unknown   _____

4. Mass of 10.00 mL of unknown   _____

5. Density of unknown   _____

6. The densities of several water-sodium chloride mixtures are reported below. On the
   accompanying piece of graph paper plot the density on the vertical axis and the % by mass
   of sodium chloride on the horizontal axis. Density and mass percent are not necessarily
   linearly related. Draw the best appropriate straight line or curve through the data.

% NaCl (by mass)	density (g/mL)
0.00	0.998
5.00	1.034
10.00	1.071
15.00	1.108
20.00	1.148
25.00	1.189

7. According to your results and the graph, what is
   the mass percent of sodium chloride in your unknown?   _____

D. Relative density of liquid and solid phases of a substance.

1. Report your observations on the liquid-solid acetophenone system.

2. Compare the acetophenone system to a liquid-solid system of water. Does one of the systems differ from intuitive expectations? Explain your answer.

3.

    a. Temperature of liquid-solid acetophenone system.   _____

    b. What significance if any, does the temperature of the liquid-solid acetophenone system have? Explain your answer.

4. Some of the *Learning Objectives* of this experiment are listed on the first page of this experiment. Did you achieve the *Learning Objectives*? Explain your answer.

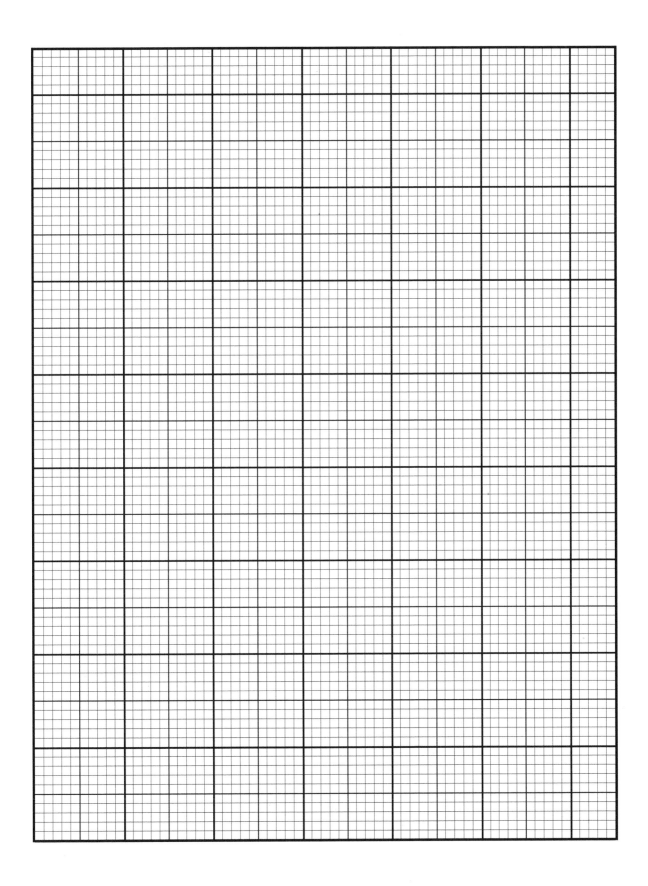

Name_____Date_____Lab Section_____

Postlaboratory Problems - *Experiment 4* - Density, Accuracy, Precision and Graphing

1. As density is an intensive property, it is very useful for identification purposes (see *Problem 3* below). Density is also a valuable unit conversion for converting volume to mass or mass to volume. The density of ethanol at 20°C is 0.789 g/mL.

    a. Calculate the mass of 25.0 mL of ethanol.   _____

    b. Suggest a situation where weighing may be preferable to a volume measurement.

    c. Calculate the volume of 25.0 g of ethanol.   _____

    d. Suggest a situation where a volume measurement may be preferable to weighing.

2. Grams and centimeters in the metric system have been defined so that the density of water at 3.98°C is exactly 1. At 20°C, the density of water is 0.9982 g/mL. What percent error results from the assumption that the density of water is 1.000 g/mL at 20°C?

                                                                _____

3. Suggest simple laboratory tests you could use to distinguish acetone, carbon tetrachloride, cyclohexane, ethyl ether and ethanol. *Appendix 1* might be helpful.

4. Describe the technique you would use to determine the density of approximately 5 gram samples of the following at 20°C and 1 atmosphere pressure:

  a. gasoline

  b. granular sugar

  c. a lump of "gold"

  d. mercury

5. In *Part D* of this experiment, the relative densities of liquid and solid acetophenone were studied and compared to the relative densities of liquid and solid water.

  a. Suggest some reasons for the choice of acetophenone for this experiment.

  b. As you undoubtedly noticed, acetophenone has an odor that is somewhat annoying. Use *Appendix 1* to see if you can select an alternative substance that could be used in this part of the experiment. Explain your answer.

6. Suggest any ways you can think of to improve any part(s) of this experiment.

EMPIRICAL FORMULAS

Joseph Proust
1754 - 1844

Learning Objectives

Upon completion of this experiment, students will have experienced:
1. The law of conservation of mass and the concept of limiting reagents.
2. A method for determining the empirical formula of an inorganic salt.
3. A method for determining the identity of an inorganic salt.
4. The determination of the percent water and empirical formula of a hydrate.
5. The use of a platinum wire flame tester.

Text Topics

Percent composition, limiting reagents, empirical formula, hydrates (see page ix).

Notes to Students and Instructor

Two empirical formula determinations are included in this experiment. The first *(Part A)* involves the determination of the formula of a compound formed from the reaction of zinc with iodine. The second *(Parts B, C, and D)* involves the determination of the numbers of waters of hydration in a hydrate. **Performance of both of these experiments will probably require more than one lab period so the instructor needs to decide if one or both of the experiments will be performed.** The instructions for the zinc iodide portion of this experiment *(Part A)* were derived from DeMeo, S., *J. Chem. Ed.*, **1995**, *72*, pp. 836 - 839. When performing *Parts B, C,* and *D, Part D-3* of this experiment should be started first and the remaining parts should be performed when time permits.

Discussion

One of the common techniques used to help determine the identity of a substance involves combustion of very small amounts of the substance. By measuring the amounts of water, carbon dioxide, and other gases produced, it is possible to determine the percentage by mass of each element in the compound. From the percentages, it is possible to calculate the empirical formula of the compound. Suppose, for example, that the combustion experiment for a compound that contains carbon, hydrogen, and oxygen gives the composition as 40.00% carbon, 6.71% hydrogen, and 53.29% oxygen by mass. Next the mass percentage needs to be converted to mole or atom ratios. Whenever dealing with percentages in a calculation of this type, one of the easiest ways to proceed is to assume that you have 100 g of the substance. Thus 100 g of the substance contains 40.00 g of carbon, 6.71 g of hydrogen and 53.29 g oxygen. As is common for many chemical calculations, the calculation of the number of moles is one of the first steps. Thinking ahead, once the number of moles is known, the ratio of moles is easily calculated.

$$40.00 \text{ g C} \left(\frac{1 \text{ mol C}}{12.011 \text{ g C}} \right) = 3.330 \text{ moles C}$$

$$6.71 \text{ g H} \left(\frac{1 \text{ mol H}}{1.008 \text{ g H}} \right) = 6.66 \text{ moles H}$$

$$53.29 \text{ g O} \left(\frac{1 \text{ mol O}}{15.999 \text{ g O}} \right) = 3.331 \text{ moles O}$$

Dividing by the lowest number of moles (3.330 moles C) gives a C:H:O ratio of 1:2:1 so the empirical formula is CH_2O. This means the compound could be glucose ($C_6H_{12}O_6$) but it could also be many other compounds including other sugars or formaldehyde. The determination of the molecular formula from the empirical formula requires an additional measurement of the molecular mass. If a molecular mass measurement for the above compound results in 150 ± 2 g/mole, the molecular formula would be calculated as $C_5H_{10}O_5$. This means the compound could be a five carbon sugar such as ribose.

molecular formula = $\dfrac{\text{molecular mass}}{\text{empirical form. mass}}$ x subscripts of empirical formula = $\dfrac{150}{30}$ x $CH_2O = C_5H_{10}O_5$

The empirical and molecular formulas can go a long way in helping to identify a compound.

Almost all ionic compounds are solids at room temperature. The crystal structure of the ionic solid consists of a repeating array, and it is not straightforward to define the smallest unit (a molecule) of the substance that still would have the properties of the substance. Thus it is better to refer to the formula mass of an ionic substance rather than its molecular mass. For the same reasons, the formula calculations for ionic compounds should be reduced to the lowest whole number ratio or the empirical formula. Except for a few unusual cases, the term molecular formula is not applicable for ionic compounds.

For metals with only one common oxidation state, it is usually possible to predict with a high degree of confidence, the empirical formula that will result from the reaction of a metal with a non-metal. For instance, based on common oxidation numbers, sodium chloride and sodium oxide should be and are NaCl and Na_2O respectively. Aluminum chloride and aluminum oxide should be and are $AlCl_3$ and Al_2O_3. When there are multiple oxidation states of a metal, more than one compound is possible. For instance, copper and oxygen form Cu_2O and CuO and more information is needed to distinguish between the two. When naming a copper oxide, it is very important that the name distinguish between the two possibilities [copper(I) oxide or cuprous oxide and copper(II) oxide or cupric oxide].

Care must be exercised as chemistry often contains wonderful surprises. Suppose the percent by mass experiment for an iron oxide results in 72.36% Fe and 27.64% by mass O. Following the procedure above results in a mole ratio of 1.296:1.727. Division by the lowest number results in a mole ratio of 1:1.33. For cases like this, the next step is to multiply by the lowest whole number that converts each of the subscripts to a whole number. Thus the formula is Fe_3O_4. As iron has two oxidation states (+2, +3), the expected formula is either FeO or Fe_2O_3. Anytime a result that is inconsistent with expectations is obtained, the first and immediate step should be to recheck all the data and calculations. In this case the result is real and Fe_3O_4 is a known compound often called magnetite. Understanding the oxidation state of iron in this compound will be left to you or your instructor but it is results like this that should not be ignored and often lead to important and exciting discoveries.

In *Part A* of today s experiment, iodine will be reacted with an excess of zinc. The masses of the starting materials, products and leftover starting material will enable you to calculate the formula of the zinc iodide produced. Since zinc in compounds has only the +2 oxidation state, the product is certainly expected to be ZnI_2. However, as noticed above for iron, expectations do not always agree with results so it is always necessary when performing a synthesis to verify the formula of the product. This will be your primary goal for *Part A* of the experiment.

Hydrates. Have you ever noticed the small envelope of chemical that sometimes comes enclosed with water sensitive products such as medicines and electronic equipment? These chemicals are desiccants; that is, they are compounds that absorb water from the air and hopefully keep the other contents of the package dry. When these inorganic compounds absorb water, they form hydrates. Precipitation of many inorganic compounds from water also often results in the incorporation of "waters of hydration" into their crystal structures. Usually the compound incorporates a specific number of water molecules per formula unit of compound. For example, the precipitation of copper(II) sulfate from water yields copper(II) sulfate pentahydrate which is written $CuSO_4 \cdot 5H_2O$. The formula of the salt is written first followed by a dot and finally the number of waters of hydration. Notice that this is the only time a coefficient is included in the formula. While hydrates do have definite formulas, the bonds to the waters are weaker than "normal" ionic and covalent bonds. This is emphasized by the use of the dot in the formula. Since the bonds are relatively weak, it is fairly easy to break them. Mild heating is often all that is necessary to decompose a typical hydrate. Decomposition reactions yield two or more distinct substances. Decomposition of a hydrate is no exception yielding the salt and water. In this experiment, you will explore some of the properties of hydrates, determine the percent by mass of water in a hydrate (simply by heating it and driving off the water) and the empirical formula (the number of waters in the formula) of a hydrate.

Compounds that absorb water from the air and can be used as desiccants are said to be hygroscopic or deliquescent. In some hydrates, the water of hydration is bonded so weakly that it tends to escape even at room temperature when the compound is exposed to the atmosphere. These compounds are efflorescent. In *Part B* of this experiment you will study the efflorescence and deliquescence of two compounds. In *Part C*, you will attempt to verify that $CuSO_4 \cdot 5H_2O$ loses water when heated.

In the *Part D* of the experiment, you will be given an unknown hydrate. Using simple qualitative tests, you will determine the identity of the salt. By quantitatively driving off the water, you will be able to calculate the mass percent of water in the hydrate. Knowing the identity of the salt, it will be possible to determine the number of waters of hydration in the formula.

To help you determine the identity of the salt, you will perform a flame test. In the flame test, a platinum wire is inserted into a solution containing the ions of interest and then inserted into a Bunsen burner flame. For some cations, the energy of the flame will cause electrons to be elevated from the ground state or lowest possible energy levels to higher energy orbitals. As this results in an unstable situation, the electron drops back to the lower energy state and gives off the excess energy often in the form of a characteristic emission of light. The color of the light is useful for the detection of the presence of ions of sodium, barium, calcium, strontium, lithium and potassium. To complete your identification, it may be necessary to attempt one single replacement reaction.

To determine the mass percent of water in the hydrate, the hydrate is weighed, heated and reweighed. The mass percent of water can be calculated from:

$$\frac{\text{weight loss during heating}}{\text{original mass}} \times 100\% = \text{mass \% water in hydrate}$$

Assume that heating of a 3.50 g sample of the hydrate of copper sulfate yields 2.25 g of anhydrous copper sulfate. The mass percent of water in the hydrate would be:

$$\left(\frac{3.50 - 2.25}{3.50}\right)(100\%) = 35.7\% \quad \text{[The theoretical value is 36.1\%]}$$

Now the ratio of the number of water molecules per formula unit of copper sulfate can be determined.

$$(2.25 \text{ g } CuSO_4)\left(\frac{1 \text{ mol}}{159.6 \text{ g } CuSO_4}\right) = 1.41 \times 10^{-2} \text{ mol } CuSO_4$$

$$(1.25 \text{ g } H_2O)\left(\frac{1 \text{ mol}}{18.02 \text{ g } H_2O}\right) = 6.94 \times 10^{-2} \text{ mol } H_2O$$

$$\frac{0.0694 \text{ moles } H_2O}{0.0141 \text{ moles } CuSO_4} = 4.92 \qquad \text{[This is within experimental error of the actual number of 5]}$$

This indicates there were 5 moles of water per mole of $CuSO_4$.

$$CuSO_4 \cdot 5H_2O(s) \longrightarrow CuSO_4(s) + 5H_2O(g)$$

Procedure

Part A - Synthesis and formula of zinc iodide. Be sure to record all masses to the limits of the balance capability. Weigh a 50 mL beaker to the nearest milligram (or if milligram balances are not available, to the nearest 0.01 g) and record the mass. Using a piece of weighing paper, weigh out about 1.2 grams of 20 mesh granular zinc and add it to the 50 mL beaker. Carefully weigh the beaker. Using a second piece of weighing paper, weigh out about 1.2 g of iodine [**Caution: iodine is toxic and should not be touched**], add it to the same 50 mL beaker and read the mass of the beaker.

Add 3 mL of 0.2 M acetic acid (acetic acid prevents the precipitation of zinc hydroxide) to the solid mixture in the beaker, swirl and observe changes of temperature and color. Continue to swirl until no further changes are evident. The beaker should have cooled back down to room temperature and the iodine and triiodide (some of the iodine and iodide combine in aqueous solution to form I_3^-) color should have disappeared. This process should take about 20 minutes.

Weigh an evaporating dish and record the mass on page 67. Carefully decant (pour off) the aqueous solution into the evaporating dish, being sure that all the leftover zinc remains in the original beaker. Add about 1 mL of 0.2 M acetic acid to the beaker (and contents), swirl and decant again into the evaporating dish. This washes the remaining zinc free of residual zinc iodide and transfers the zinc iodide to the evaporating dish. Repeat the washing process two more times. Wash the zinc three more times with 0.2 M acetic acid and discard these additional washings but save the beaker and the remaining zinc.

Mount the evaporating dish in a 400 mL beaker containing about 200 mL of water on a wire gauze above a Bunsen burner as shown in *Figure 5-1*. Heat the beaker until the contents of the evaporating dish appear to be dry. Achieving apparent dryness with steam heating can consume considerable time. Time can be saved if you move to the next step before dryness is completely attained. Carefully remove the beaker with beaker tongs and place the evaporating dish directly on the wire gauze. **Very** gently flame the dish until crackling stops and the solid in the dish turns slightly off-white. Excessive heating results in spattering and/or a dark yellow color indicating that the product is decomposing to iodine. **Both of these problems need to be avoided.** Allow the dish to cool and weigh it. Repeat the direct heating, cooling and weighing cycle until constant mass is achieved (within at least 0.01 grams).

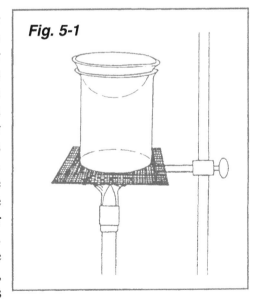

Fig. 5-1

Now flame the beaker containing the zinc until it is dry. Allow it to cool and weigh it. Repeat the heating, cooling and weighing cycle until constant mass is achieved (within at least 0.01 grams).

Optional enhancement. _____ Dissolve about 0.1 gram of the white solid that remains from the aqueous solution in 2 mL of water on a watch glass. Obtain a battery clip (e.g., Radio Shack 270-325) that has had two copper leads attached to the ends of the clip wires. Attach the clip to a 9-volt battery and insert the two copper leads into the solution. Record your observations.

Parts B, C and D are a unit involving hydrates.

B. Deliquescence and efflorescence. Place a few crystals of sodium sulfate decahydrate on a watch glass. Occasionally observe their appearance for about an hour and write an equation for the observed change. On another watch glass, place a few crystals of potassium acetate. As before, observe their appearance over at least a one hour time period.

C. Copper(II) sulfate pentahydrate. Put 1.0 g of $CuSO_4 \cdot 5H_2O$ into a 13 x 100 mm test tube. Stuff a small wad of fine glass wool *(Caution: Minimize contact of the glass wool with your hands - it causes splinters and itching)* into the test tube so that it holds copper(II) sulfate pentahydrate in place when the tube is tilted downward. Clamp the test tube upside down over a watch glass. Holding the base of the burner, heat the $CuSO_4 \cdot 5H_2O$. The blue color should begin to dissipate while the vapors given off condense to a liquid. If any sign of blackening occurs, reduce the heat. Heat until several drops of liquid have been collected and the residue is white.

Using an eyedropper, test a drop of the liquid collected in the watch glass with a piece of blue cobalt chloride test paper (if the paper is pink, pass it quickly high over the burner flame to dry it and turn it blue). Test a drop of water on a piece of blue cobalt chloride paper.

Remove the glass wool plug with a wire hook, break up the white residue with a stir rod or wire and pour it into another watch glass *(caution: avoid letting this powder come into contact with your skin)*. Using a spatula, divide the powder into two piles. Test one pile with a drop of liquid collected in the watch glass. Test the other pile with a drop of water. Write equations for the observed changes.

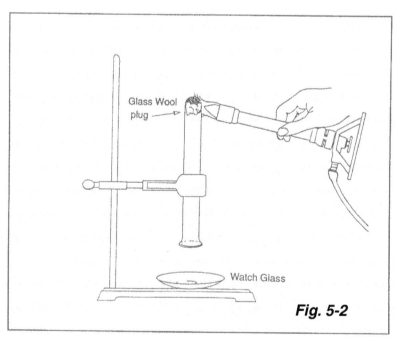

Fig. 5-2

D. Analysis and percent water of an unknown hydrate.

1. Your unknown is a hydrate of strontium chloride, magnesium sulfate or zinc sulfate. Dissolve a small amount (about 0.1 g) in about 5 mL of deionized water in a test tube to use for *#1* and *#2*. Clean a platinum wire by alternately dipping it into 6 M HCl and inserting into the flame until little or no color is observed. Perform flame tests on known solutions of $ZnSO_4$, $MgSO_4$ and $SrCl_2$ and finally the solution of the unknown being sure to clean the wire between each test. This test should enable you to either identify strontium ion or rule it out.

2. If your unknown is not strontium chloride, drop a short piece of magnesium ribbon into your unknown solution. Allow 30 seconds for a reaction to take place. If the magnesium ribbon tarnishes, your unknown is zinc sulfate.

$$Mg(s) \ + \ ZnSO_4(aq) \ = \ MgSO_4(aq) \ + \ Zn(s)$$

If no reaction other than bubbling occurs ($Mg(s) + MgSO_4(aq)$ = no reaction), the unknown is magnesium sulfate. The bubbling is due to a side reaction of the magnesium with water.

$$Mg(s) + \ 2\,H_2O(l) \ = \ Mg(OH)_2(s) \ + \ H_2(g)$$

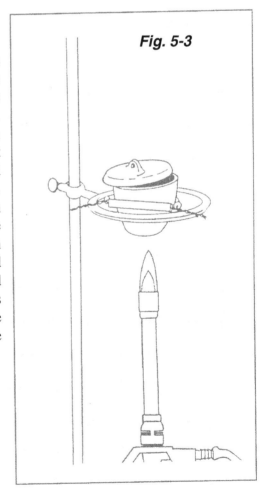

Fig. 5-3

3. Weigh a clean, dry crucible and cover to at least the nearest 0.01 g (preferably 0.001 g). Place about 4 grams (3.5 - 4.5) of your unknown hydrate crystals in the crucible and weigh to at least the nearest 0.01 g. Suspend the crucible in a clay triangle over a Bunsen burner. Heat gently with the top *slightly ajar* for about eight minutes and then vigorously (the crucible should glow a dull orange) for an additional eight minutes. Allow the crucible to cool (about 5 minutes), and weigh it to at least the nearest 0.01 g. Heat the crucible vigorously again for about 5 minutes, cool and weigh again. If the mass difference between the first and second heatings is greater than 0.01 g, perform a third heating, cooling, weighing cycle. Repeat the process until two successive weighings do not differ by more than 0.01 g. Calculate the mass percent of water and the empirical formula of the hydrate.

Name_____Date_____Lab Section_____

Prelaboratory Problems - *Experiment 5* - Empirical Formulas
The solutions to the starred problems are in *Appendix 4*.

1.* 5.0 g of aluminum and 5.0 g of oxygen are reacted and yield the expected product.

    a. Write a balanced equation for the reaction.

    b. Which one of the two reagents was used in excess and how much of it remains after the reaction is complete (the other reagent is called the limiting reagent).

                                                                   _____

                                                                   _____

2. 2.20 grams of chromium reacts with excess oxygen to give 3.22 grams of a chromium oxide. What is the name and formula of the chromium oxide? Write a balanced equation for the reaction.

                                                                     _____

                                                                     _____

3. Complete and balance the following equations:

    a.* $\qquad BaCl_2 \cdot 2H_2O_{(s)} \ -\Delta->$

    b. $\qquad Co(C_2H_3O_2)_2 \cdot 4H_2O_{(s)} \ -\Delta->$

4. What is the percent by mass of water in:

    a.* $\qquad BaCl_2 \cdot 2H_2O$ _____

    b. $\qquad Co(C_2H_3O_2)_2 \cdot 4H_2O$ _____

5.* Determine the empirical formula and the molecular formula of a compound (Freon 11) that consists of 8.74% C, 77.43% Cl, 13.83% F and has a molecular mass of 137 g/mol.

                                                                      _____

                                                                        _____

6. A compound consists of 40.00% carbon, 6.71% hydrogen and 53.29% oxygen and has a molecular mass of 180 ± 1 g/mole. Determine the empirical and molecular formulas of the compound.

      _____

      _____

7. The mass percent of water in a hydrate of $MnCl_2$ is 36.41%. What is the empirical formula of the hydrate?

      _____

8.* A 4.00 gram sample of a hydrate of nickel(II) bromide loses 0.793 grams of water when heated. Determine the mass percent water in the hydrate and the formula of the hydrate.

      _____

      _____

9. A 2.500 gram sample of a hydrate of calcium sulfate loses 0.523 grams of water when heated. Determine the mass percent of water in the hydrate and the formula of the hydrate.

      _____

      _____

10. An unknown solution containing one of the salts $ZnSO_4$, $MgSO_4$ or $SrCl_2$ gives a negative flame test but tarnishes a piece of magnesium inserted into the solution. Which salt was in the solution?

      _____

Name_____Date_____Lab Section_____

Results and Discussion - *Experiment 5* - Empirical Formulas

A. Synthesis and formula of zinc iodide.

1. Write the expected balanced equation
   for the reaction between zinc and iodine _____

2. Mass of beaker _____

3. Mass of evaporating dish _____

4. Mass of iodine _____

5. Mass of zinc _____

6. Mass of zinc + iodine _____

7. Observations after addition of water containing acetic acid

8. Mass of beaker + residual zinc _____ _____ _____

               trial 1   trial 2   trial 3 if necessary

9. Mass of residual zinc _____

10. Mass of zinc consumed in reaction _____

11. Mass of evap. dish + zinc iodide _____ _____ _____

                trial 1   trial 2   trial 3 if necessary

12. Mass of zinc iodide _____

13. a.   Mass of zinc iodide + residual zinc _____

    b.   Was mass conserved within experimental error in this reaction?
    Explain your answer.

14. Moles of zinc consumed in reaction _____

15. Moles of iodine consumed in reaction _____

16. Mole ratio of iodine to zinc (use appropriate number of significant figsures) _____

17. Formula of zinc iodide _____

18. Does your experimental formula agree with the expected formula? Explain your answer.

19. In terms of the chemistry and energy of the reaction, explain your observations in #7 above.

20. Explain why some zinc was left over at the end of the reaction and why you think the amounts were selected to have zinc left over.

21. (optional) What did you observe in the electrolysis reaction?

22. (optional) Were your observations on the electrolysis consistent with your expectations? Explain your answer.

B. Deliquescence and efflorescence.

System	Observations	Reaction

1. $Na_2SO_4 \cdot 10H_2O$

2. $KC_2H_3O_2$ $KC_2H_3O_2(s) + n\ H_2O(l) = KC_2H_3O_2 \cdot n\ H_2O(s)$

C. Copper(II) sulfate pentahydrate

System	Observations	Reaction

1.   water + $CoCl_2$ paper
     (forms the hydrate $CoCl_2 \cdot 6H_2O$)

2.   condensate + $CoCl_2$ paper

3.   water + $CuSO_4$

4.   condensate + $CuSO_4$

5.   What evidence supports the conclusion that the condensate is water?

D. Analysis and percent water of an unknown hydrate.

1.   Unknown #   _____

2.   Flame tests   solution   flame color

                                       $SrCl_2$ _____

                                       $ZnSO_4$ _____

                                       $MgSO_4$ _____

                                       unknown   _____

     Flame test conclusion _____

3.   Mg + unknown → observations _____

     Reaction _____

4.   Unknown: $SrCl_2$ or $ZnSO_4$ or $MgSO_4$ _____

5.
   a. Mass of crucible + cover   _____

   b. Mass of crucible + cover + unknown   _____

   c. Mass of crucible + cover + unknown after first heating   _____

   d. Mass of crucible + cover + unknown after second heating   _____

   e. Mass of crucible + cover + unknown (after third heating if necessary)   _____

   f. Mass of crucible + cover + unknown (after fourth heating if necessary) _____

   g. Mass of original unknown   _____

   h. Mass of water lost by unknown   _____

   i. Mass percent of water in unknown   _____

   j. Mass of unknown salt remaining after heating   _____

   k. Formula mass of anhydrous salt   _____

   l. Moles of anhydrous unknown salt   _____

   m. Formula mass of water   _____

   n. Moles of water lost   _____

   o. Ratio of moles of water to moles of unknown
       (use appropriate number of significant figures)   _____

   p. Formula of unknown hydrate   _____

   q. Unknown identification number   _____

6.   Some of the *Learning Objectives* of this experiment are listed on the first page of this experiment. Did you achieve the *Learning Objectives*? Explain your answer.

CLASSIFICATION OF CHEMICAL REACTIONS

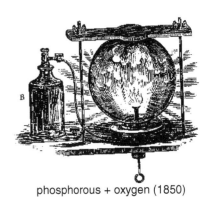

phosphorous + oxygen (1850)

Learning Objectives

Upon completion of this experiment, students will have experienced:
1. Five of the common types of chemical reactions.
2. The completion and balancing of chemical equations.
3. The observation of some chemical properties of hydrogen and oxygen.
4. An introduction to concepts of stoichiometry.

Text Topics

The classification of chemical reactions, prediction of reaction products, balancing equations (for correlation with some textbooks, see page ix).

Notes to Students and Instructor

The use of Beral pipets to generate hydrogen and oxygen was derived from an experiment in a text by David Ehrenkranz and John J. Mauch [*Chemistry in Microscale*, Kendall/Hunt. Co., Dubuque (1960)].

Discussion

The process of classification often assists with the simplification and solution of problems. Classification of diseases by cause; viral, bacterial or fungal, facilitates proper treatment. The sciences are frequently classified into disciplines such as physics, chemistry, biology and geology. Then chemistry is often subdivided into organic, inorganic, analytical, theoretical and physical branches. Attempts have been made to classify reactions by type. Later in the course, you will learn how to determine if a reaction is an oxidation-reduction reaction. Today, we will run several reactions and attempt to classify them by the nature of the reaction: combination, decomposition, combustion, single replacement or double replacement.

Combination: the reaction of two substances to form one substance.

$$C_{(s)} + O_{2(g)} = CO_{2(g)}$$

$$MgO_{(s)} + H_2O_{(l)} = Mg(OH)_{2(s)}$$

$$SO_{3(g)} + H_2O_{(l)} = H_2SO_{4(l)}$$

$$SrCl_{2(s)} + 6H_2O_{(l)} = SrCl_2 \cdot 6H_2O_{(s)}$$

Decomposition: The reverse of combination or the breaking down of one substance into two or more substances.

$$H_2CO_{3(aq)} = H_2O_{(l)} + CO_{2(g)}$$

$$HgO_{(s)} = Hg_{(l)} + \tfrac{1}{2}O_{2(g)}$$

$$Ca(HCO_3)_{2(aq)} = CaCO_{3(s)} + H_2O_{(l)} + CO_{2(g)}$$

$$Mg(OH)_{2(s)} = MgO_{(s)} + H_2O_{(g)}$$

$$SrCl_2 \cdot 6H_2O_{(s)} = SrCl_{2(s)} + 6H_2O_{(l)}$$

Combustion: The rapid reaction of a compound with oxygen. Some combustion reactions are also combination reactions and vice versa.

$$2CH_4O_{(l)} + 3O_{2(g)} = 2CO_{2(g)} + 4H_2O_{(g)}$$

$$2C_8H_{18(l)} + 25O_{2(g)} = 16CO_{2(g)} + 18H_2O_{(g)}$$

Single Replacement: The replacement of an element in a compound by another element originally in elemental form.

reaction	*observation*
$Cu_{(s)} + 2AgNO_{3(aq)} = Cu(NO_3)_{2(aq)} + 2Ag_{(s)}$	plating of metallic silver on copper and appearance of blue color in solution
$Mg_{(s)} + H_2SO_{4(aq)} = MgSO_{4(aq)} + H_{2(g)}$	gas evolution
$Br_{2(aq)} + 2KI_{(aq)} = 2KBr_{(aq)} + I_{2(aq)}$	loss of red bromine color and appearance of brown iodine color

Double Replacement: An exchange of positive and negative partners by two compounds (most commonly involving two ionic compounds) in aqueous solution. These reactions usually proceed when at least one of the products is a compound insoluble in water (precipitate), a gas or a compound that decomposes into a gas, or a slightly ionized compound.

reaction	*observation*
$3\,BaCl_2(aq) \;+\; 2\,Na_3PO_4(aq) \;=\; Ba_3(PO_4)_2(s) \;+\; 6\,NaCl(aq)$	white ppt.
$K_2CO_3(aq) \;+\; 2\,HNO_3(aq) \;=\; 2\,KNO_3(aq) \;+\; H_2O(l) \;+\; CO_2(g)$	gas
$H_2SO_4(aq) \;+\; 2\,KOH(aq) \;=\; K_2SO_4(aq) \;+\; 2\,H_2O(g)$	heat

In addition to recording observations about a reaction and classifying the reaction by type, one should write a balanced chemical equation for any reactions that occur. The examples above are all balanced.

The first step in writing a balanced equation is to write the correct formulas for reactants and products. Once this is done, subscripts ***must not be changed*** to balance the equation as this changes the substance. Balance the equation using coefficients (numbers in front of the formula). A coefficient denotes the relative number of moles of the substance whose formula it precedes. Locate the formula with the largest subscript (not subscripts within a polyatomic ion but subscripts that give the number of atoms or ions per formula unit). For the reaction below, 8 is the largest subscript.

$$C_3H_8(g) \;+\; O_2(g) \;\rightarrow\; CO_2(g) \;+\; H_2O(g)$$

Imagine the coefficient 1 in front of the propane (C_3H_8) and balance the hydrogens and then the carbons.

$$1\,C_3H_8(g) \;+\; O_2(g) \;\rightarrow\; 3\,CO_2(g) \;+\; 4\,H_2O(g)$$

Observe that there are now ten oxygen atoms on the right and that there are two oxygen atoms in an oxygen molecule on the left. Divide the number of atoms needed (10) by the number per molecule or formula unit (2) to arrive at the correct coefficient (5).

$$C_3H_8(g) \;+\; 5\,O_2(g) \;=\; 3\,CO_2(g) \;+\; 4\,H_2O(g)$$

Notice that coefficient of 1 is not written in the final equation but is understood. Also notice the very common technique of leaving the O_2 (or H_2) until last if it is present. The coefficient for O_2 affects the amount of one element only whereas the other coefficients change the amounts of at least two elements.

For double replacement reactions, start with the ion with the largest subscript. In case of a tie, choose the ion with the largest oxidation number. For the reaction below,

$$BaCl_2(aq) + Na_3PO_4(aq) \rightarrow Ba_3(PO_4)_2(s) + NaCl(aq)$$

Na^+ and Ba^{2+} have subscripts of 3 but Ba^{2+} has the higher charge. Notice that the subscript 4 is part of the phosphate polyatomic ion and is not part of this consideration. Start with the Ba^{2+} and work from one side of the equation to the other. Balance the barium ions on the left side of the equation by inserting a coefficient of 3.

$$3 BaCl_2(aq) + Na_3PO_4(aq) \rightarrow 1 Ba_3(PO_4)_2(s) + NaCl(aq)$$

The coefficient of 3 in front of $BaCl_2$ locked in 6 chlorides so a 6 is now needed in front of NaCl on the right.

$$3 BaCl_2(aq) + Na_3PO_4(aq) \rightarrow 1 Ba_3(PO_4)_2(s) + 6 NaCl(aq)$$

The 6 locks in 6 sodiums so the coefficient in front of Na_3PO_4 is the number needed (6) divided by the number per formula unit (3) resulting in a coefficient of 2. Finally check to see if the phosphates are balanced to be sure you haven't made an error.

$$3 BaCl_2(aq) + 2 Na_3PO_4(aq) = Ba_3(PO_4)_2(s) + 6 NaCl(aq)$$

Procedure

A. Classification of reactions. Carry out the reactions as instructed. Record all your observations (precipitate, gas evolution, heat evolution, or color change). Use your observations, the nature of the reactants and the examples given in the *Discussion* section to classify the reactions by type. In particular, be alert for combination reactions when two compounds react to form one, decomposition when one compound decomposes into two or more compounds, combustion when a compound reacts with oxygen, single replacement when an element reacts with a compound to give another element and compound, double replacement when two compounds react to give two new compounds (detectable by formation of a precipitate, a gas, or heat evolution). After mixing, touch the exterior of each test tube to check for heat evolution. Write balanced equations for all observed reactions. If a reaction is not detected, write "NAR" for no apparent reaction. Be sure to give each mixture ample time (at least 5 minutes) before concluding there is no apparent reaction (by vision and/or touch). For sample analyses of reactions, see the *Prelaboratory Problems.*

1. Mix 3 mL of 0.1 M $CaCl_2$ with 2 mL of 0.1 M Na_3PO_4.

2. Add a few drops of water to a test tube containing about 0.5 g $CuSO_4$ (anhydrous). *[Caution: Anhydrous copper sulfate (white color) is corrosive. Avoid skin contact but wash with copious quantities of water if contact occurs.]*

3. Heat a test tube containing about 0.5 g $Cu(OH)_2$ with a burner.

4. To a test tube containing 3 mL of 6 M HCl, add a 1 cm^2 piece of zinc ribbon. If a gas evolves, quickly insert a lighted splint into the mouth of the test tube. Balance the equations for both reactions.

5. Mix 2 mL of 3M HCl with 2 mL of 1 M Na_2CO_3 (Note that in this case, two types of reactions occur, one right after the other).

6. To a test tube containing 3 mL of 3% H_2O_2 (hydrogen peroxide), add 0.1 g of the catalyst MnO_2. (Note that a catalyst affects the rate of a reaction but is not involved in the overall reaction for the process).

7. Add 2 mL of a saturated calcium acetate solution (about 35 g/100 mL H_2O) to an evaporating dish. To the dish add 15 mL of ethanol and swirl the contents. Pour off any excess liquid and ignite the remaining contents with a match. For an additional effect, sprinkle some boric acid on the mixture. Although the reaction is actually more complex, assume that the reactants in this reaction are only ethanol (C_2H_5OH) and oxygen.

8. Add 3 g of NH_4Cl and 7 g of $Sr(OH)_2 \cdot 8H_2O$ to a 125 mL Erlenmeyer flask and swirl vigorously for about 5 minutes. Be sure to record all observations including odor, sounds and touch (flask, not contents) sensations in addition to visual.

9. Mix 2 mL of 3 M H_2SO_4 with 4 mL of 3 M NaOH.

10. Mix 2 mL of 0.1 M $CaCl_2$ with 2 mL of 0.1 M Na_2CO_3.

11. To a test tube containing 3 mL of 0.1 M $CuSO_4$, add a 1 cm^2 piece of zinc ribbon.

12. To a test tube containing 3 mL of 0.1 M $ZnSO_4$, add a 1 inch long piece of copper wire.

13. Mix 1 mL of 0.1 M $CaCl_2$ and 2 mL of 0.1 M $NaNO_3$.

14. Heat a test tube containing about 2 g of $CuSO_4 \cdot 5H_2O$ with a burner.

15. Mix 2 mL of 6 M HCl with 4 mL of 3 M NaOH.

B. Beral pipet rockets. Reactions similar to those performed earlier (*A-4* and *A-6*) to generate hydrogen and oxygen will be explored further and then used for the propulsion system for rockets made from Beral pipets. Because of the potentially explosive nature of hydrogen - oxygen mixtures, the small volumes provided by Beral pipets are ideally suited for these experiments.

Step 1. Prepare 2 test tube gas generators (see *Figure 6-1*). One will be used in *Steps 1 - 8* and *12, 13* as a hydrogen generator. The second will be used in *Steps 9 - 13* as an oxygen generator.

a.   Cut off the stem of a graduated Beral pipet (e.g., Flinn Scientific # AP 1516) about 1 cm from the bulb. The bulb will be referred to as the "collection bulb".

b.   Cut the tip of the pipet stem at a point just before the diameter begins to get smaller and insert its tip into a #2 one hole rubber stopper as shown. Place the stopper in a 20   150 mm test tube.

Step 2. Add about 200 mL of water to a 400 mL beaker. This will be used as a temperature regulator during the generation of hydrogen and oxygen.

Step 3. Fill the collection bulb with water by holding it (opening upward) under water in a dish pan, squeezing the air out and allowing water to enter.

Step 4. Add about 8 grams of 20 mesh granular zinc to one of the gas generator tubes.

Step 5. Light a candle.

Step 6. Add 25 mL of 3 M hydrochloric acid to the test tube containing the zinc and stopper it with the #2 stopper device. Put the tube in the 400 mL beaker of water and wait 10 seconds before beginning the next part (see *Figure 6-2*). [Note: If gas generation slows during the experiment, replace the hydrochloric acid but do not replace the zinc]

Step 7. Put the collection bulb over the pipet tip (nozzle) and collect hydrogen until all the water has been displaced from the bulb.

Step 8. Remove the bulb from the hydrogen generator and squirt the hydrogen you collected into the candle flame (*Figure 6-3*). Repeat the hydrogen collecting and squirting once or twice and report your observations.

Step 9. Add about 7 grams of manganese metal to the second (oxygen) generator tube, label it and fill another collection bulb as in *Step 3*.

Step 10. Add 25 mL of 3% hydrogen peroxide to the oxygen generating tube and put this tube in the beaker of water next to the hydrogen generator tube. [Note: If gas generation slows during the experiment, replace the 3% hydrogen peroxide but do not replace the manganese metal.

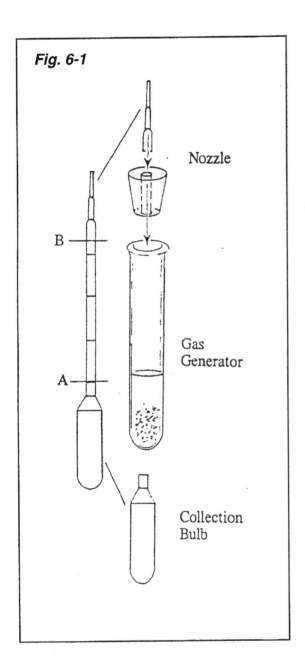

Fig. 6-1

Nozzle

B

A

Gas
Generator

Collection
Bulb

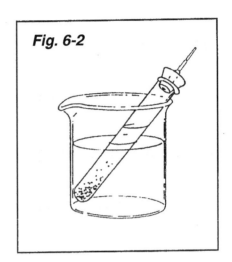

Fig. 6-2

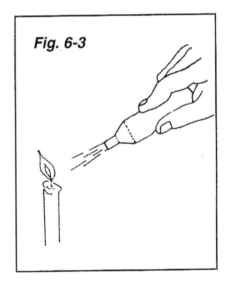

Fig. 6-3

Step 11. Collect a bulb full of oxygen as in *step 7* and squirt the oxygen into the candle flame. Repeat this process a couple of times and report your observations.

Step 12. Now collect half a bulb full of hydrogen, remove the bulb from the hydrogen generator and put it on the oxygen generator until all the water is displaced from the bulb. This should give a 50/50 mixture of hydrogen and oxygen. Squirt the gas mixture into the candle flame and report your observations. Repeat the experiment with several different ratios of hydrogen to oxygen and try to find the optimum mixture.

_____ Refill the pipet with the optimum mixture and convert your pipet to a rocket by placing it on the rocket launcher. A rocket launcher can be made by putting a nail through a piece of cardboard, attaching a piece of wire (about 0.5 meters) to the head of the nail (sort of a ground) and putting the "collection bulb rocket" over the point of the nail (*Figure 6-4*). The rocket can be launched by bringing a Tesla coil up to bottom (narrow part) of the rocket so that the spark jumps through the plastic to the nail. [***Caution: Because of potential hazards of electric shock from the coil, the instructor should launch all rockets.***] Have a contest with the other students in the class to determine who can make the farthest flying rocket. Try varying the takeoff angle (nail angle) and the nail diameter (the larger the diameter without creating friction, the better in our experience). **Also try leaving some water in the rocket.**

Step 14. When you are finished with the experiment, place the unreacted manganese and zinc in the appropriate strainers (in the sink). These metals can be reused.

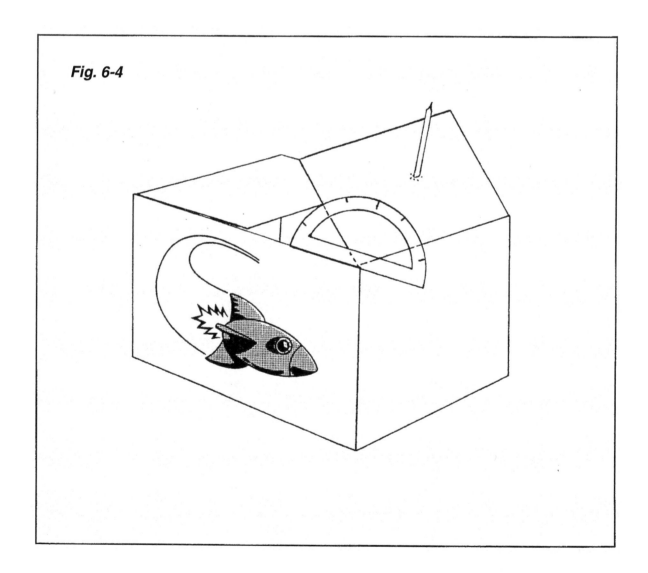

Fig. 6-4

Name_____Date_____Lab Section_____

Prelaboratory Problems - *Experiment 6* - Classification of Chemical Reactions
The solutions to the starred problems are in *Appendix 4*.

1. Classify the following reactions according to combination (CA), decomposition (D), combustion (CU), single replacement (SR) or double replacement (DR) and then balance the equations.

reaction   **classification**

a.* ____$Mg(s)$ + ____$ZnCl_2(aq)$ = ____$MgCl_2(aq)$ + ____$Zn(s)$ _____

b.* ____$AgNO_3(aq)$ + ____$CaCl_2(aq)$ = ____$AgCl(s)$ + ____$Ca(NO_3)_2(aq)$ _____

c.* ____$C_2H_6(g)$ + ____$O_2(g)$ = ____$CO_2(g)$ + ____$H_2O(g)$ _____

d.* ____$Na_2O(s)$ + ____$H_2O(l)$ = ____$NaOH(aq)$ _____

e.* ____$KClO_3(s)$ = ____$KCl(s)$ + ____$O_2(g)$ _____

f. ____$Al(s)$ + ____$HCl(aq)$ = ____$AlCl_3(aq)$ + ____$H_2(g)$ _____

g. ____$C_3H_6O(g)$ + ____$O_2(g)$ = ____$CO_2(g)$ + ____$H_2O(g)$ _____

h. ____$Fe(s)$ + ____$O_2(g)$ = ____$Fe_2O_3(s)$ _____

i. ____$Cl_2(aq)$ + ____$KBr(aq)$ = ____$Br_2(aq)$ + ____$KCl(aq)$ _____

j. ____$Ca(NO_3)_2(aq)$ + ____$K_3PO_4(aq)$ = ____$Ca_3(PO_4)_2(s)$ + ____$KNO_3(aq)$ _____

k. ____$Ca(HCO_3)_2(aq)$ = ____$CaCO_3(s)$ + ____$H_2O(l)$ + ____$CO_2(g)$ _____

l. ____$NaOH(aq)$ + ____$H_3PO_4(aq)$ = ____$Na_3PO_4(s)$ + ____$H_2O(aq)$ _____

2. Complete, balance and classify the following reactions:

a.* ____$BaCl_2(aq)$ + ____$Na_2SO_4(aq)$ =   _____

b.* ____$Fe(s)$ + ____$CuCl_2(aq)$ =   _____

c.* ____$C_6H_6(l)$ + ____$O_2(g)$ =   _____

reaction	**classification**

d.* ___BaCl$_2$(s) + ___H$_2$O(l) =   _____

e. ___Pb(NO$_3$)$_2$(aq) + ___K$_2$CrO$_4$(aq) =   _____

f. ___Mg(s) + ___H$_2$SO$_4$(aq) =   _____

g. ___CaO(s) + ___H$_2$O(l) =   _____

h. ___C$_2$H$_4$O(l) + ___O$_2$(g) =   _____

i. ___HNO$_3$(aq) + ___Ba(OH)$_2$(aq) =   _____

j. ___HCl(aq) + ___KHCO$_3$(aq) =   _____

3.   The Haber process for the preparation of ammonia involves a combination reaction between
      nitrogen and hydrogen.

      a.*   Write a balanced molecular equation for the reaction.

      b.*   Give the optimum nitrogen to hydrogen mole ratio for the reaction.   _____

      c.   Could the following figures be used as a model for the Haber reaction? Explain your
             answer.

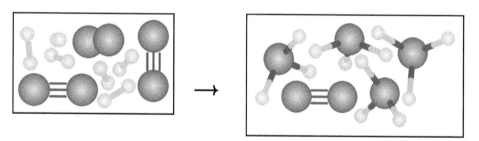

4.   The contact process for the preparation of sulfuric acid involves a combination reaction
      between sulfur dioxide and oxygen to form sulfur trioxide.

      a. Write a balanced molecular equation for the reaction.

      b. Give the optimum sulfur dioxide to oxygen mole ratio for the reaction.   _____

Name_____Date_____Lab Section_____

Results and Discussion - *Experiment 6* - Classification of Chemical Reactions

A. Classification of reactions. For each system record significant observations (e.g., white precipitate, gas evolution, heat evolution, color change, or *NAR* for no apparent reaction). For numbers 1-9 classify the potential reaction according to combination (CA), decomposition (D), combustion (CU), single replacement (SR), double replacement (DR) and balance the equations. For numbers 10-15, record observations and complete, balance and classify any reactions that occur.

reaction	**observations**	**class.**

1.

____$CaCl_2$(aq) + ____Na_3PO_4(aq) = ____$Ca_3(PO_4)_2$(s) + ____NaCl(aq)   _____   _____

2.

____$CuSO_4$(s) + ____H_2O(l) = ____$CuSO_4 \cdot$__H_2O(s)   _____   _____

3.

____$Cu(OH)_2$(s) = ____CuO(s) + ____H_2O(g)   _____   _____

4.

____Zn(s) + ____HCl(aq) = ____$ZnCl_2$(aq) + ____H_2(g)   _____   _____

____H_2(g) + ____O_2(g) = ____H_2O(g)   _____   _____

5.

____HCl(aq) + ____Na_2CO_3(aq) = ____NaCl(aq) + H_2O(l) + CO_2(g)   _____   _____

6.

____H_2O_2(aq) = ____H_2O(l) + ____O_2(g)   _____   _____

7.

____C_2H_6O(l) + ____O_2(g) = ____CO_2(g) + ____H_2O(g)   _____   _____

8.

____$Sr(OH)_2 \cdot 8H_2O$(s) + ____NH_4Cl(s) = ____$SrCl_2$(aq) + ____NH_3(aq) + ____H_2O(l)

_____   _____

| **reaction** | **observations** | **class.** |

9.

____H_2SO_4(aq) + ____NaOH(aq) = ____Na_2SO_4(aq) + ____H_2O(l) _____   _____

*   *   *   *   *   *   *   *   *   *   *   *   *

10.

____$CaCl_2$(aq) + ____Na_2CO_3(aq) =

11.   _____   _____

____Zn(s) + ____$CuSO_4$(aq) =

12.   _____   _____

____Cu(s) + ____$ZnSO_4$(aq) =

13.   _____   _____

____$CaCl_2$(aq) + ____$NaNO_3$(aq) =

14.   _____   _____

____$CuSO_4 \cdot 5H_2O$(s) =

15.   _____   _____

____HCl(aq) + ____NaOH(aq) =

                                                                          _____   _____

B. Beral pipet rockets

1. Write a balanced chemical equation for the reaction between zinc and hydrochloric acid.

2. What did you observe when the hydrogen was "squirted" into the flame?

3. Write a balanced chemical equation for the reaction of hydrogen in the flame.

4. Write a balanced chemical equation for the decomposition of hydrogen peroxide into oxygen and water (The surface of manganese had air oxidized, prior to its use, to manganese dioxide. MnO_2 catalyzes the decomposition of H_2O_2. But do not include manganese or manganese dioxide in the balanced equation.).

5. What did you observe when the oxygen was "squirted" in to the flame? Explain your observation.

6. Rate the report from each of the hydrogen - oxygen mixtures on a loudness scale of 1 to 10 with 10 being very loud and 1 being no report.

hydrogen/oxygen ratio   rating

_____   _____

_____   _____

_____   _____

_____   _____

_____   _____

7. What mixture seemed to give the loudest reports? Is this result consistent with the ratio predicted by the balanced equation (*#B-3*)? Explain your answer.

8. Could the figures below serve as a model for any of the mixtures you tested above? Explain your answer.

9. Describe the results of your rocket launch. What parameters affect the flight distance?

10. Suggest any ways you can think of to improve any part(s) of this experiment.

11. Some of the *Learning Objectives* of this experiment are listed on the first page of this experiment. Did you achieve the *Learning Objectives*? Explain your answer.

QUANTITATIVE PRECIPITATION

Antoine Lavoisier
1743 - 1794 (guillotined)

Learning Objectives

Upon completion of this experiment, students will have experienced:
1. Gravity filtration.
2. Stoichiometric calculations.

Text Topics

Formula mass, the mole, hydrates, stoichiometry, experimental yield, theoretical yield, percent yield (for correlation to some textbooks, see page ix).

Notes to Students and Instructor

While the laboratory manipulations of this experiment should not require more than two hours, the best results are obtained if the product is dried several hours and preferably overnight before the final weighing. It is recommended that students return the day after lab for the final weighing.

Discussion

The addition of hydroxide ions to a solution containing copper(II) ions results in the precipitation of copper(II) hydroxide. Subsequent heating *in situ* of the copper(II) hydroxide results in decomposition to copper(II) oxide and water. The CuO can be quantitatively filtered, dried and weighed.

If a weighed amount of a soluble copper(II) compound is used in this procedure, it is possible to calculate the amount of copper(II) oxide that should be formed (the theoretical yield). The experimental yield can be compared with the theoretical yield to calculate the percent yield.

Assuming the procedure is quantitative, the technique can be utilized to determine the mass percent of copper in an unknown copper(II) compound or in a mixture. If the compound or mixture is water soluble and addition of hydroxide ions results in a copper(II) hydroxide precipitate only, the mass determination of copper(II) oxide enables a calculation of the amount of copper in the original sample to be made.

Procedure

Weigh between 1.8 and 2.0 grams of copper(II) sulfate pentahydrate into a 250 mL beaker to the nearest milligram. Add 10 mL of deionized water to the beaker and dissolve the copper salt. Add 10 mL of 6.0 M NaOH to the solution with stirring. Place a watch glass over the beaker and heat the mixture to the boiling point. Try to avoid spattering especially onto the watch glass. If spattering occurs, use a wash bottle to wash all the solid back down into the solution. Heat until all of the blue solid has been decomposed to copper(II) oxide and water (a few minutes). Allow the mixture to cool before filtering.

Fold a 12.5 cm diameter piece of Whatman #1 filter paper (see *Figure 7-1*). Tear off a small outside corner of the paper to improve filtering. Weigh and record the mass of the paper. Place the paper in a long stemmed funnel (see *Figure 7-1*), wet the paper with deionized water from a wash bottle and transfer the previously heated mixture to the filter. Be sure not to overload the filter (the liquid should not rise to less than 0.5 cm from the top of the paper). Be patient and add small portions. While you are filtering, begin the preparation of the second sample for filtration (see bottom paragraph). After all liquid has been transferred to the funnel, use a wash bottle to direct spurts of water at the remaining solid in the beaker and transfer this mixture to the funnel. Continue this procedure until virtually all the solid has been transferred. Now wash the precipitate once more with water and allow it to filter through until dripping ceases. Discard the filtrate which should be colorless and not contain any precipitate. Carefully lift out the paper and unfold it on a watch glass. Place the watch glass in an 105°C oven for a minimum of 3 hours (preferably overnight). Remove and weigh. Calculate the percent yield.

Repeat the above procedure with a 1.8 - 2.0 gram sample of an unknown copper(II) compound supplied by your instructor. Determine the mass percent of copper in the sample.

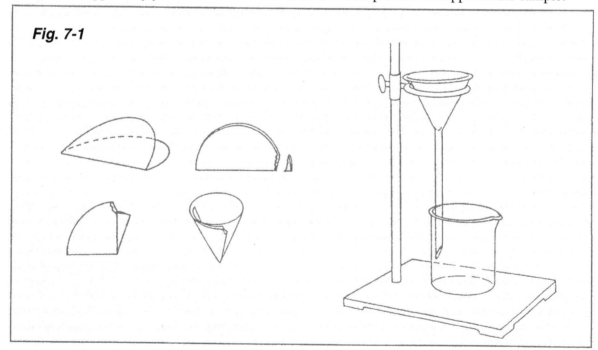

Fig. 7-1

Name_____Date_____Lab Section_____

Prelaboratory Problems - *Experiment 7* - Quantitative Precipitation
The solutions to the starred problems are in *Appendix 4*.

1. Calculate the number of moles in:

   a.* 33 grams of carbon dioxide   _____

   b. 12.7 grams of iodine   _____

   c. 0.777 grams of cobalt(II) sulfate heptahydrate   _____

2. Calculate the mass in grams of:

   a.* 3.45×10^{-2} moles of silver nitrate   _____

   b. 8.76×10^{-3} moles of sodium acetate trihydrate   _____

3. For the reactions below that are predicted to go (see *Appendix 3*), write balanced equations. Otherwise write *NAR*.

   a.* magnesium nitrate + sodium hydroxide

   b. barium chloride + sodium hydroxide

   c. zinc chloride + sodium hydroxide

4.* 2.3 grams of sodium reacts violently with excess water and 0.080 grams of hydrogen gas are collected. What are the theoretical and percent yields of hydrogen gas?

5. 1.7 g of benzoic acid ($C_7H_6O_2$) is reacted with an excess of methanol in the presence of a catalyst and 1.7 g of methyl benzoate ($C_8H_8O_2$) is obtained (the mole ratio of benzoic acid to methyl benzoate is 1:1). What are the theoretical and percent yields of methyl benzoate?

6. 2.500 grams of a solid mixture contains barium chloride and sodium chloride. The solid is dissolved in water and an aqueous solution containing an excess of sulfate ions is added. A precipitate is formed, collected, dried and is determined to weigh 2.123 grams. What was the mass percent of barium chloride in the original sample?

7. A 2.50 gram sample of an unknown silver salt (possibly $AgClO_3$, $AgClO_4$, $AgNO_3$ or AgF) is dissolved in water. An excess of HCl solution is added and 1.88 g of AgCl is collected. Determine the identity of the silver salt.

Name_____Date_____Lab Section_____

Results and Conclusions - *Experiment 7* - Quantitative Precipitation

1. Write a balanced molecular equation for the reaction between aqueous copper(II) sulfate and sodium hydroxide.

2. Write a balanced molecular equation for the decomposition of copper(II) hydroxide with heating.

3. Write the overall equation for the process starting with copper(II) sulfate pentahydrate and ending with copper(II) oxide.

4. Calculation of the theoretical yield and percent yield of CuO.

    a. Mass of beaker + $CuSO_4 \cdot 5H_2O$ _____

    b. Mass of empty beaker   _____

    c. Mass of $CuSO_4 \cdot 5H_2O$ _____

    d. Formula mass of $CuSO_4 \cdot 5H_2O$ _____

    e. Moles of $CuSO_4 \cdot 5H_2O$ _____

    f. Theoretical number of moles of CuO   _____

    g. Formula mass of CuO   _____

    h. Theoretical yield in grams of CuO   _____

    i. Mass of filter paper + CuO after drying   _____

    j. Mass of filter paper   _____

    k. Experimental mass of CuO   _____

    l. Percent yield of CuO   _____

    m. Percent deviation between experimental and theoretical yields   _____

n. Show the series of unit conversions that one could use to calculate the theoretical yield in grams of CuO from the grams of $CuSO_4 \cdot 5H_2O$.

5. Calculation of the mass percent of copper in the unknown.

   a. Unknown number   _____

   b. Mass of beaker + unknown   _____

   c. Mass of beaker   _____

   d. Mass of unknown   _____

   e. Mass of filter paper + CuO   _____

   f. Mass of filter paper   _____

   g. Mass of CuO   _____

   h. Moles of CuO   _____

   i. Grams of copper in CuO (and unknown)   _____

   j. Mass percent of copper in unknown   _____

6. Your unknown was one of the following copper(II) compounds: $CuBr_2$, $CuCl_2 \cdot 2H_2O$, $Cu(NO_3)_2 \cdot 3H_2O$.

   a. Calculate the mass percent of copper in each of the possible unknowns.

   $CuBr_2$ _____

   $CuCl_2 \cdot 2H_2O$ _____

   $Cu(NO_3)_2 \cdot 3H_2O$ _____

   b. Identify your unknown. Explain your answer.   _____

7. Some of the *Learning Objectives* of this experiment are listed on the first page of this experiment. Did you achieve the *Learning Objectives*? Explain your answer.

Name_____Date_____Lab Section_____

Postlaboratory Problems - *Experiment 7* - Quantitative Precipitation

1. Critically evaluate the procedure used in this experiment as a quantitative technique for the analysis of copper(II) ion. Suggest sources of errors and ways of minimizing the errors.

2. Why must the CuO precipitate in the funnel be thoroughly washed with water?

3. Could this procedure be used to determine the mass percent of copper in a sample that also contains magnesium ions? Explain your answer (see *Prelaboratory Problem 3* in this experiment).

4. Several criteria need to be satisfied for quantitative precipitation to be a useful analytical technique. Suggest procedures that might work for the analyses of the samples below or give reasons why the analysis might be very difficult. Assume that at least 1 gram samples are available unless stated otherwise.

a.   the percent of barium in a solid mixture of sodium chloride and barium chloride

b. the percent of silver in a solid mixture of sodium chloride and silver chloride

c.   the percent of sodium in a solid mixture of sodium chloride and potassium chloride

d.   the percent of copper in 1.00×10^{-3} grams of a mixture containing soluble copper and sodium salts

5. What would the consequences have been in this experiment if you had used 10 mL of 0.1 M NaOH instead of 10 mL of 6.0 M NaOH?

6. Suggest any ways you can think of to improve any part(s) of this experiment.

ELECTRICAL CONDUCTIVITY AND ELECTROLYTES

Gas conductance test
W. Magnus, 1850

Learning Objectives

Upon completion of this experiment, students will have experienced:
1. The determination of the electrical conductivity of solids and solutions.
2. A study of the nature of chemical bonding.
3. A study of conductivity change during chemical reaction.

Text Topics

Electrical conductivity, covalent and ionic bonding, double replacement reactions, dissociation of bonds in solution (for correlation to some textbooks, see page ix).

Discussion

Electricity was discovered even before John Dalton set forth the modern concept of the atomic nature of matter (1804). The observation that electricity can travel through matter such as wires (or even your body under unfortunate and shocking circumstances), suggests that ***matter might be electrical in nature.*** In fact, later in the 19th century, scientists probing the nature of electrical beams were able to demonstrate that atoms of all elements are composed of protons and electrons (the discovery of the other particle common to all atoms, the neutron, was not made until 1932). Can you imagine what your life would be like without electricity? 39% of our energy consumption is used for production of electricity (actual conversion to electricity is only about 35% efficient). Have you ever wondered how electricity flows through wires and how your body can serve as an electrical conductor? We will discuss electrical conductance and then use experimental conductance determinations to probe the nature of bonding in several compounds.

For an electrical current there must be a flow of charge. In solid conductors such as copper wire which have metallic bonding, some electrons are held very loosely in the lattice and are relatively free to flow. A current, however, does not consist of continuous movement of the same electrons but is more like a domino effect where one electron moves a short distance before colliding with and transferring its energy to the next electron. Once this electron domino effect is set in motion by an energy source such as a battery or a generator, the flow continues with only a little resistance in metals. Resistance does cause loss and conversion of the electrical energy to heat. Nonmetals do not have loose electrons. They impede electron flow and are electrical insulators.

Passage of a current through a solution occurs in a rather different way. Pure water only conducts under extreme conditions but aqueous solutions containing ions can be good conductors. For conduction to occur in solution, cations must migrate to the negative electrode (cathode) and accept electrons while simultaneously anions migrate to the positive electrode (anode) and deposit electrons. The net result of the double migration is a flow of electrons from the anode to the cathode and completion of the circuit.

The question remains concerning how the solution is provided with a sufficient number of ions to conduct a current. Compounds are composed of two or more elements held together by attractive forces called chemical bonds. Your text will focus attention on two types of bonds, ionic (the electrostatic attraction between cations and anions) and covalent (sharing of a pair of electrons). When ionic compounds dissolve in water, dissociation occurs into hydrated cations and anions that are potential conductors.

$$NaCl(s) \longrightarrow_{H_2O} Na^+ + Cl^-$$

If the ionic compound has sufficient solubility in water, then the solution will be conductive and the compound is called an *electrolyte.* Except for acids and bases, the dissolving of covalently bonded compounds (molecules) in water does not result in formation of ions. Most molecules are therefore nonelectrolytes. Strong acids with very polar covalent bonds totally dissociate in water and like like soluble ionic compounds are strong electrolytes.

$$HCl(g) \longrightarrow_{H_2O} H^+ + Cl^-$$

It should be noted that H^+ is a shorthand notation for hydrated protons and H_3O^+ is probably a better representation of the species present. Afterall, H^+ is simply a proton and the concentrated charge certainly attracts solvent molecules to it.

Weak acids and bases only partially dissociate in water and are usually fair to poor electrolytes.

$$HC_2H_3O_2(l) \qquad \longrightarrow_{H_2O} H^+ + C_2H_3O_2^-$$

$$NH_3(g) + H_2O(l) \longrightarrow NH_4^+ + OH^-$$

The strong bases you will encounter in this course (e.g., sodium hydroxide) are ionic compounds and strong electrolytes.

How can you predict if the bonding is ionic or covalent? As the electronegativity difference between the partners increases, the ionic character of the bond increases. For our purposes here, assume that metal-nonmetal bonds and metal-polyatomic ion bonds are ionic and nonmetal-nonmetal bonds are covalent.

In this experiment, the conductance of several solutions will be studied to determine if the bonding present in the solute is ionic, covalent or covalent with the potential for ion formation.

In addition to studying the conductivities of aqueous solutions containing single compounds, three of the studies will involve the monitoring of conductivity as a second compound is added. For the three examples, double replacement reactions will occur. In double replacement reactions, positive and negative ions switch partners.

$$AgNO_3(aq) \ + \ NaCl(aq) \ = \ NaNO_3(aq) \ + \ AgCl(s)$$

This might result in formation of electrolytes from weak electrolytes or nonelectrolytes from electrolytes.

Procedure

A. Conductivity of solids. A simple device for testing conductivity can be constructed from a 9 volt battery, battery clips, a 1 kiloohm resister and a T 1¾ LED (e.g., Radio Shack 276-041). A light bulb is not satisfactory for testing solution conductance. You will either be supplied with the circuit or the parts to construct one. Test the circuit to check its integrity by touching the probes together. The LED should glow. Now test the conductance of the solids listed in the **Results and Discussion** section.

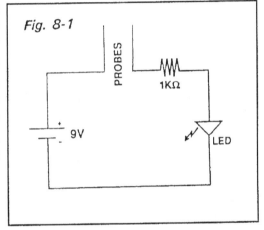

B. Conductivity of solutions. Test the conductance in 50 or 100 mL beakers of the solutions listed in the **Results and Discussion** section. Use sufficient solution for conductance measurements with your apparatus (typically about 5 to 25 mL of solution) and attempt to be consistent with the amount of the solution and the technique you apply. For the three samples with a special notation (4, 12 and 14), be sure to follow the additional instructions. For numbers 12 and 14, try to start with volumes of 10 mL or less if possible to minimize the amount of dropwise addition required.

Prelaboratory Problems - *Experiment 8* - **Electrical Conductivity and Electrolytes**

Before beginning the laboratory manipulations, predict in the ***Results and Discussion*** section which solids and solutions will be strong conductors or electrolytes (SC or SE), fair conductors or electrolytes (FC or FE), weak conductors or electrolytes (WC or WE) or nonconductors or nonelectrolytes (NC or NE). Also predict what your observations will be for the experiments involving the monitoring of the conductivity to follow the progress of a chemical reaction.

Examples: Acetone (CH_3COCH_3) has only covalent bonds. The addition of acetone to water will not add any ions to the water and the solution will not conduct. Sodium nitrate which has ionic bonding is a strong electrolyte and hydrobromic acid (covalently bonded but a strong acid) is also a strong electrolyte. Ant venom (formic acid) is a covalently bonded weak acid and is a fair electrolyte. Barium hydroxide is ionic and sufficiently soluble in water to be a strong electrolyte. If sulfuric acid is added dropwise to a barium hydroxide solution while the conductivity is continuously monitored, the conductivity will gradually decrease.

$$Ba(OH)_2(aq) + H_2SO_4(aq) = BaSO_4(s) + 2 H_2O(l)$$

As indicated by the above double replacement reaction, one product is insoluble in water and the other is the nonelectrolyte, water. When the equivalence point is reached, there should not be any ions left in the solution and the solution should be nonconductive. However, continued addition of the strong acid, sulfuric acid, after the equivalence point has been reached should lead to an increase in the number of ions in solution and the conductance should return.

Name_____Date_____Lab Section_____

Results and Discussion - *Experiment 8* - **Electrical Conductivity and Electrolytes**

A. **Conductivity of solids** (Mark SC, FC, WC, or NC for strong, fair, weak or non-conductor)

Solid	Prediction	Observed Conductivity
aluminum	_____	_____
copper	_____	_____
glass rod	_____	_____
pencil lead	_____	_____
plastic strip	_____	_____
wood splint	_____	_____

B. **Conductivity of solutions** (Mark SE, FE, WE, or NE for strong, fair, weak or non electrolyte)

#	Solution	Prediction	Observed Conductivity	
1.	0.1 M NaCl	_____	_____	
2.	1×10^{-2} M NaCl	_____	_____	
3.	1×10^{-3} M NaCl	_____	_____	
4.	crystalline NaCl	_____	_____	(go to #21)
5.	deionized water	_____	_____	
6.	tap water	_____	_____	
7.	0.1 M glucose	_____	_____	
8.	0.1 M ethanol	_____	_____	
9.	0.1 M NaOH	_____	_____	
10.	0.1 M NH_3	_____	_____	
11.	0.1 M HCl	_____	_____	
12.	0.1 M $HC_2H_3O_2$ (≤ 10 mL)	_____	_____	(go to # 22)
13.	0.1 M H_2SO_4	_____	_____	
14.	saturated $Ca(OH)_2$ (10 mL)	_____	_____	(go to # 23)

To answer exercises 15 - 20 below, compare, contrast and explain
your observations for the indicated exercises.

15. #1, 4

16. #1, 2, 3

17. #1, 5, 6

18. #1, 7, 8

19. #1, 9, 10

20. #1, 11, 12

For systems 21 - 23, predict what your observations will be when the instructions are followed. Perform the experiment, record and explain your observations utilizing net ionic equations when appropriate.

21. While monitoring conductivity of initially crystalline NaCl, add water dropwise with stirring until all of the NaCl has dissolved.

Predictions:

Observations:

Explanation and net ionic equation:

22. While monitoring the conductivity of 0.1 M $HC_2H_3O_2$ (preferably 10 mL or less), add 0.1 M NH_3 dropwise with stirring until an approximately equal volume of 0.1 M NH_3 has been added.

Predictions:

Observations:

Explanation, molecular and net ionic equations:

23. While monitoring the conductivity of 10 mL of a saturated calcium hydroxide solution, add 40 drops of 0.5 M H_3PO_4, mixing after each addition. Check the conductivity after the addition of each drop.

Predictions:

Observations:

Explanation, molecular and net ionic equations:

24. Suggest any ways you can think of to improve any part(s) of this experiment.

25. Some of the *Learning Objectives* of this experiment are listed on the first page of this experiment. Did you achieve the *Learning Objectives*? Explain your answer.

9

IONIC REACTIONS

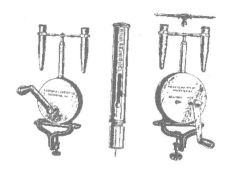

1880 centrifuges

Learning Objectives

Upon completion of this experiment, students will have experienced:
1. The balancing of double replacement equations.
2. The derivation and writing of net ionic equations.
3. The development of schemes for the analysis of unlabeled bottles and identification of cations in a mixture.

Text Topics

Formula equations, net ionic equations, solubility of ionic compounds, double replacement reactions (for correlation to some textbooks, see page ix).

Notes to Students and Instructor

It is very important that students derive schemes for the two challenges in this experiment prior to beginning the laboratory manipulations.

Discussion

In the conductivity experiment, the behavior of ionic and covalently bonded compounds in aqueous solution was explored. You observed and studied double replacement reactions in *Experiments 1* and *6* and monitored conductivity at different stages of two double replacement reactions in *Experiment 8*. You should be acquiring the experience needed to enable you to predict if a potential double replacement reaction will go and the observations that should accompany it. This experiment will add to that experience.

When two aqueous solutions are mixed, each containing an ionized or partially ionized compound, a double replacement reaction is possible.

$$MX + NY = MY + NX$$

However, generally only those with at least one of three potential driving forces (formation of an insoluble product, formation of a gas, formation of a weakly ionized compound) actually result in chemical change. Examples of the three common driving forces are given below along with the observation that usually accompanies the reaction.

$$Cu(NO_3)_2(aq) + 2\,NaOH(aq) = Cu(OH)_2(s) + 2\,NaNO_3(aq)$$

blue ppt.

$$2\,HCl(aq) + Na_2CO_3(aq) = 2\,NaCl(aq) + H_2O(l) + CO_2(g)$$

gas

$$HNO_3(aq) + NaOH(aq) = NaNO_3(aq) + H_2O(l) + \text{heat}$$

For solubility information, reference to solubility tables (e.g., *Appendix 3*) is often necessary but it is useful to remember that nitrates, acetates, ammonium compounds and compounds of the Group IA elements are generally soluble. The three most commonly encountered insoluble compounds in textbooks are silver chloride, barium sulfate and calcium carbonate. Except for CO_2 (from H_2CO_3), SO_2 (from H_2SO_3), H_2S and NH_3, gas evolution will generally not be observed because almost all ionic compounds are solids at room temperature. The most commonly encountered weakly ionized compounds are water, acetic acid and ammonia.

An alternative method to determine if a reaction will go is to derive its net ionic equation. To do this recall from the conductivity experiment that ionic compounds and strong acids totally ionize in water.

$$NaCl \quad -_{H_2O}\!\!\rightarrow\ Na^+ + Cl^-$$

$$K_2SO_4 \quad -_{H_2O}\!\!\rightarrow\ 2\,K^+ + SO_4^{2-}$$

$$HCl \quad -_{H_2O}\!\!\rightarrow\ H^+ + Cl^-$$

To arrive at a net ionic equation (until you have considerable experience), start by writing a total ionic equation. Write all **totally** ionized, **dissolved** chemicals in ionic form. Leave insoluble compounds and weakly ionized compounds in molecular form and do not break up polyatomic ions. For example, water (H_2O), acetic acid ($HC_2H_3O_2$) and formulas of insoluble compounds ($BaSO_4$) are written intact but dissolved, ionic compounds such as sodium phosphate are written as ions ($3\,Na^+ + PO_4^{3-}$).

For the reaction between copper(II) nitrate and sodium hydroxide:

$$Cu(NO_3)_2(aq) + 2\,NaOH(aq) = 2\,NaNO_3(aq) + Cu(OH)_2(s)$$

the total ionic equation is:

$$Cu^{2+} + 2\,NO_3^- + 2\,Na^+ + 2\,OH^- = 2\,Na^+ + 2\,NO_3^- + Cu(OH)_2(s)$$

Note that the subscripts that are not part of a polyatomic formula become coefficients. The product, $Cu(OH)_2$, is written in molecular form as it is insoluble in water. When you see an algebraic equation in the form $a + b = a + c$, you would subtract a from both sides of the equation leaving $b = c$. The process going from the total ionic to the net ionic equation is the same as with the algebraic equation. Sodium and nitrate ions are unchanged in the reaction (spectator ions) and are dropped leaving the net ionic equation:

$$Cu^{2+} + 2\,OH^- = Cu(OH)_{2(s)}$$

This equation and all net ionic equations are of great importance because they enable you to focus on the actual chemical change that occurs. Try to write the net ionic equation for the double replacement reaction between HCl and Na_2CO_3 by first writing the total ionic equation and then eliminating the spectator ions. You should obtain:

$$2\,H^+ + 2\,Cl^- + 2\,Na^+ + CO_3^{2-} = H_2O_{(l)} + CO_{2(g)} + 2\,Na^+ + 2\,Cl^-$$

$$2\,H^+ + CO_3^{2-} = H_2O_{(l)} + CO_{2(g)}$$

Make sure when you are finished that the elements and charges are balanced. For cases where no reaction should occur, the algebraic form of the net ionic equation should end up $0 = 0$!

Because it is usually possible to correctly predict observations and products for double replacement reactions, it is often possible to develop schemes for the qualitative analysis of cations and anions and this will be the topic of today's experiment.

Procedure

A. **Unlabeled bottles.** The challenges that follow will be considerably facilitated if you develop prediction schemes prior to performing the laboratory exercise. The first experiment includes a set of seven bottles labeled only *A to G*. The identities of the solutions they contain are listed in the ***Results and Discussion*** section. (Note: mixtures of any two can undergo only double replacement reactions (possibly followed by decomposition) although several will not react at all). Your challenge is to assign correct names to each bottle based on a comparison of a prediction matrix with an experimental matrix. You are allowed to mix the contents of any of the bottles but no other reagents, test papers or solutions are permitted. To enable you to solve this problem and to develop your ability to write double replacement equations and net ionic equations, you should complete the prediction equations and matrix on pages 109 - 112 before beginning this lab. For example, what should be observed if barium chloride is mixed with sodium sulfate? First write and balance the double replacement reaction:

$$BaCl_{2(aq)} + Na_2SO_{4(aq)} = BaSO_{4(s)} + 2\,NaCl_{(aq)}$$

Next ask if either of the products is insoluble, a weakly ionized compound or a gas or a compound that decomposes into a gas. As both products in this case are ionic and almost all ionic compounds are solids at room temperature, the only question that needs further consideration concerns solubility. Either from memory or a table (for example, see *Appendix 3*) you should conclude that barium sulfate is insoluble and a reaction will take place. The net ionic equation is:

$$Ba^{2+} + SO_4^{2-} = BaSO_{4(s)}$$

By studying and comparing the pattern of precipitates, gas and heat evolution, you should be able to assign identities to the seven bottles. Pay special attention to unique observations such as heat or gas evolution. These observations can considerably narrow down the choices. Experimentally, one approach is to pour about 2 mL of A into 6 test tubes and add 2 mL of B to the first tube, two mL of C to the second and so on being sure to mix and observe each tube with each addition.

B. Qualitative analysis. The second challenge requires even a little more creativity on your part. You will be provided with a solution containing the cations Li^+, Mg^{2+}, Na^+, and Sr^{2+}. Your goal is to develop a scheme for detecting the presence of each ion in the mixture. In addition to using a solubility table (see *Appendix 3*) and observing double replacement reactions, you will need to make use of flame tests. Also you will probably find that to test for at least one of the ions, it will first be necessary to remove other ions that would interfere with your proposed test. To do this you might want to use a centrifuge.

Flame tests. The energy provided by a Bunsen burner flame is capable of promoting the ground state electrons of some elements to higher energy orbitals resulting in an excited state. For some cations, the return of the exited electron to the ground state results in the emission of a characteristically colored flame.

Ion	Color
barium	green
calcium	red-orange
lithium	red
potassium	violet (masked by sodium - use cobalt glass)
sodium	yellow-orange
strontium	red
zinc	greenish-white (weak)

To perform a flame test, first adjust the flame to a pure blue. Then clean a platinum wire by alternately inserting it into dilute (6M) HCl and into the flame until the insertion yields little or no flame color. Now dip the wire into a test solution, hold it in the flame and observe the color. Try this with solutions containing each of the possible ions, Li^+, Mg^{2+}, Na^+, and Sr^{2+} and a mixture of all four. Be sure to clean the wire each time you change test solutions.

Centrifuge. Centrifuging is a quick method for separating liquid from solid and is especially useful for small volumes such as you will have in this experiment. Often in qualitative analysis schemes, it is necessary to remove ions that would interfere with other tests by precipitating them out of solution. When a precipitate is formed, the solution is centrifuged. The decantate is poured off into a clean test tube and tested again with the precipitating agent. If further precipitation occurs, centrifuging is required again. Otherwise the decantate is ready for continued testing. The precipitate is washed with water to remove soluble ions, centrifuged and the wash liquid is discarded. Washing should be repeated two times. The presence of the precipitate may be conclusive enough evidence for the presence of an ion. Or the precipitate, now that it is free of other ions, may be redissolved (often by acid) and subjected to confirmatory testing.

Lets consider as an example a solution that could contain Ag^+, Ba^{2+}, Cu^{2+} and Na^+. A blue color should indicate the presence of copper(II) and a colorless solution its absence. Examination of *Appendix 3* reveals that of the possible ions, only Ag^+ forms an insoluble chloride. If addition of HCl to the mixture yields a white precipitate, Ag^+ is present. After centrifuging, the precipitate should be properly disposed of and the decantate tested with sodium sulfate solution. If barium ion is present, a precipitate will form. Again the precipitate can be discarded and the decantate tested with sodium hydroxide. A precipitate or absence thereof should confirm the earlier conclusion about copper(II). Now a flame test may be run on the original sample to check for sodium ion. The bright yellow-orange sodium flame should be visible and may mask the flames of barium and/or copper. A flow diagram should be constructed to help keep track of the sequence.

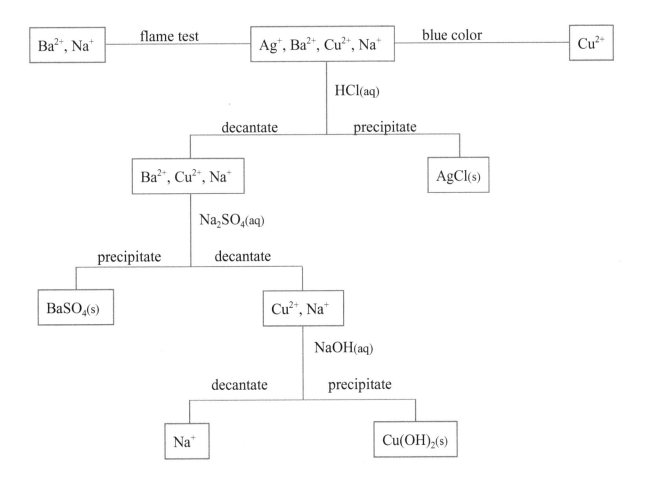

Now, for the ions, Li^+, Mg^{2+}, Na^+ and Sr^{2+}, develop a scheme and write a flow diagram for your scheme. Test the scheme on a mixture containing all four cations. If it works, obtain an unknown from your instructor that could contain 1 to 4 of the cations and analyze it. Otherwise, modify your scheme and try again.

Important and useful tips. Lithium phosphate, while fairly insoluble is slow to form at room temperature. All solutions in **Parts A and B** suspected of containing lithium phosphate should be heated in a hot water bath. This considerably speeds up the precipitation process. Also, strontium hydroxide is marginally soluble and formation of a precipitate is usually slow and dependent on the amounts of reagents used. However, the slight cloudy precipitate that results might be useful for characterizing the precipitate. The mixture of sulfuric acid with potassium phosphate gives a slightly exothermic reaction. The attention given to the nature of this reaction is up to the instructor. Also we have found that commercial potassium phosphate is sometimes contaminated with carbonate and alert students observe some bubbling from the reaction of the contaminant, potassium carbonate, with sulfuric acid.

Name_____Date_____Lab Section_____

Prelaboratory Problems - *Experiment 9* - Ionic Reactions
The solutions to the starred problems are in *Appendix 4*.

1.* Patients with gastrointestinal pain are often given a "milk shake" containing barium sulfate to drink and then they are fluoroscoped. Barium salts are very toxic. Why doesn't barium sulfate kill the patient and why is it used?

2. The labels of bottles that contain barium hydroxide, hydrochloric acid and sodium carbonate had fallen off. When the contents of bottle *A* were mixed with *B's* contents, a white precipitate formed, *A* with *C* yielded a gas and *B* with *C* gave heat. Identify *A*, *B*, *C* and write molecular and net ionic equations for the chemical changes observed.

3. These questions deal with the scheme for Ag^+, Ba^{2+}, Cu^{2+} and Na^+ discussed in the *Procedure* section.

   a.* Could addition of sodium sulfate be used in the first step? Explain your answer.

   b. Could addition of sodium hydroxide be used in the first step? Explain your answer.

4.   Write molecular and net ionic equations and fill in the prediction matrix before coming to lab for *reactions 1 - 21* on pages 109- 112.

5.   Develop an analysis scheme and flow diagram before coming to lab and fill it in on page 114.

Name_____Date_____Lab Section_____

Results and Discussion - *Experiment 9* - Ionic Reactions

A. Unlabeled bottles. Seven unlabeled bottles containing the solutions below in some scrambled sequence will be provided.

1.5 M H_2SO_4	0.1 M $Mg(NO_3)_2$	3 M NaOH
1 M K_3PO_4	1 M Na_2CO_3	0.1 M $SrCl_2$
0.5 M Li_2SO_4		

For the 21 possible mixtures of the seven solutions, write formula (FE), total ionic (TIE) and net ionic (NIE) equations. When no reaction is expected, write *NAR* for no apparent reaction. Based on these equations, fill in the prediction matrix. Based on your experimental observations, fill in the observation matrix. Compare the two and assign identities to *A - G*. (For solubilities, see *Appendix 3*)

1. sulfuric acid + potassium phosphate

   FE   _____

   TIE   _____

   NIE   _____

2. sulfuric acid + lithium sulfate

   FE   _____

   TIE   _____

   NIE   _____

3. sulfuric acid + magnesium nitrate

   FE   _____

   TIE   _____

   NIE   _____

4. sulfuric acid + sodium carbonate

    FE   _____

    TIE   _____

    NIE   _____

5. sulfuric acid + sodium hydroxide

    FE   _____

    TIE   _____

    NIE   _____

6. sulfuric acid + strontium chloride

    FE   _____

    TIE   _____

    NIE   _____

7. potassium phosphate + lithium sulfate

    FE   _____

    TIE   _____

    NIE   _____

8. potassium phosphate + magnesium nitrate

    FE   _____

    TIE   _____

    NIE   _____

9. potassium phosphate + sodium carbonate

    FE   _____

    TIE   _____

    NIE   _____

10. potassium phosphate + sodium hydroxide

   FE   _____

   TIE   _____

   NIE   _____

11. potassium phosphate + strontium chloride

   FE   _____

   TIE   _____

   NIE   _____

12. lithium sulfate + magnesium nitrate

   FE   _____

   TIE   _____

   NIE   _____

13. lithium sulfate + sodium carbonate

   FE   _____

   TIE   _____

   NIE   _____

14. lithium sulfate + sodium hydroxide

   FE   _____

   TIE   _____

   NIE   _____

15. lithium sulfate + strontium chloride

   FE   _____

   TIE   _____

   NIE   _____

16. magnesium nitrate + sodium carbonate

   FE _____

   TIE _____

   NIE _____

17. magnesium nitrate + sodium hydroxide

   FE _____

   TIE _____

   NIE _____

18. magnesium nitrate + strontium chloride

   FE _____

   TIE _____

   NIE _____

19. sodium carbonate + sodium hydroxide

   FE _____

   TIE _____

   NIE _____

20. sodium carbonate + strontium chloride

   FE _____

   TIE _____

   NIE _____

21. sodium hydroxide + strontium chloride

   FE _____

   TIE _____

   NIE _____

Prediction Matrix

	K₃PO₄	Li₂SO₄	Mg(NO₃)₂	Na₂CO₃	NaOH	SrCl₂	
	1	2	3	4	5	6	H₂SO₄
		7	8	9	10	11	K₃PO₄
			12	13	14	15	Li₂SO₄
				16	17	18	Mg(NO₃)₂
					19	20	Na₂CO₃
						21	NaOH

Experimental Observation Matrix

	B	C	D	E	F	G	
							A
							B
							C
							D
							E
							F

label color _____

A = _____   D = _____   F = _____

B = _____   E = _____   G = _____

C = _____

B. Qualitative Analysis.

1. Prepare a flow diagram for the analysis of the cations, Li^+, Mg^{2+}, Na^+, and Sr^{2+}.

$$Li^+, Mg^{2+}, Na^+, Sr^{2+}$$

2. List the steps of your procedure for your known (a mixture of all four cations) followed by your observations and molecular and net ionic equations that account for your observations.

Procedure

<u>Observations (for the known)</u>   <u>Equations</u>

3. Give your observations and conclusions for your unknown.

4. Cations present in your unknown (unknown # = _____), _____

5. Suggest any ways you can think of to improve any part(s) of this experiment.

6. Some of the *Learning Objectives* of this experiment are listed on the first page of this experiment. Did you achieve the *Learning Objectives*? Explain your answer.

10

THERMOCHEMISTRY

Herman von Helmoltz
1821 - 1894 (ΔH)

Learning Objectives

Upon completion of this experiment, students will have experienced:
1. The determination of the enthalpy of a reaction.
2. Endothermic and exothermic processes.
3. Hess's law using experimental data and Internet data.

Text Topics

Endothermic and exothermic processes, enthalpy, Hess's law, (see page ix).

Notes to Students and Instructor

This experiment can be done with a thermometer and manual graphing or more conveniently with a temperature probe connected to a computer interface coupled with the appropriate software.

Discussion

Combustion is probably the most commonly run chemical reaction. The controlled burning of coal, oil and gasoline to produce energy has enabled us to progress quickly into today's technologically based society. Unfortunately, our haste to progress has not always been accompanied by enough consideration for the environmental impact of our actions. If our population continues to increase and if we continue to use nonrenewable resources at our present rate, we could jeopardize our future quality of life. As part of our priorities, we need to develop alternative sources of energy that should have a lower environmental impact such as nuclear fusion and solar voltaic cells. For the short term, combustion will continue to be our primary source of energy and it is important that we understand the energetics of combustion and other chemical reactions.

A consideration of the overall energy balance of a reaction enables us to determine if a reaction can go (is it spontaneous?). The overall energetics of a reaction can often be accurately calculated from a rather short compilation of parameters available in most chemistry handbooks. This provides an extremely powerful technique for determining optimum conditions for a reaction. Generally the most important part of the overall energetics is the enthalpy or heat content of the reaction. We call reactions that consume thermal energy, endothermic (positive enthalpy or the sign of ΔH is +) and those that evolve thermal energy, exothermic (negative enthalpy or the sign of ΔH

is −). This experiment will focus on the determination of the enthalpy changes of several processes of interest to chemists. Recognize that enthalpy is not the only energy factor that determines spontaneity. Entropy sometimes also plays an important role.

Specific heat. To determine the enthalpy of a process, the mass, temperature change, and the specific heat of the components are needed. The specific heat of a substance is the amount of energy required to raise the temperature of one gram of the substance one degree Celsius. For water, with its many unusual properties (such as the density decrease with freezing), it would appear that its very high specific heat of 1.00 cal. gram^{-1} K^{-1} or 4.184 joules gram^{-1} K^{-1} (compared with the values for most other substances - metals are 0.1 to 0.8 joules gram^{-1} K^{-1}) is again another unique and unusual property. However, as you will discover in *Parts b* and *c* of *Prelaboratory Problem 4*, the value is completely consistent with the values for other substances and theory. Today you will use the value for the specific heat of water in an experiment to determine the specific heat of a metal. The specific heat values necessary for enthalpy calculations for other substances will also be provided.

Enthalpies of solution and reaction. The change in enthalpy for a process is a convenient thermodynamic property for laboratory study because it is the change in heat content at constant pressure. As most laboratory experiments are conducted open to the atmosphere, the pressure is constant for the process. If the temperature change for a process can be measured and the mass and specific heat of the system are known; $\Delta H = mC_p\Delta T$ (m = mass, C_p = specific heat of substance, ΔT = temperature change). There are at least two basic complications to this procedure. First the system changes temperature in a container and the container also changes temperature and absorbs or evolves energy. Today you will run the reactions in polystyrene cups. Although it is possible to correct for the "calorimetry constant" of the cup, our experiments indicate the error in the cup corrections are as large as the error itself. We will therefore assume a calorimetry constant of zero and recognize that more accurate measurements would need to take the constant for the cup into account.

Second, changes in the system are not instantaneous. Time is consumed mixing the reactants and it takes time to read thermometers. Thermal energy is lost during the mixing process and this causes some error. You will correct for these errors by plotting temperature versus time and extrapolating to the time of mixing.

Enthalpy of formation. For a chemical reaction, your text will develop the concept of Hess's law. Hess's law is a powerful predictive tool as it enables you with a short table of values for heats of formation of substances to calculate the heats of reaction for a long list of chemical reactions. The heat of reaction ΔH_r is the difference between the sum of the heats of formation of the products and reactants:

$$\Delta H_r = \Sigma[n\Delta H_{f(products)}] - \Sigma[n\Delta H_{f(reactants)}] \qquad \text{(n = moles of substance or coefficient in balanced equation)}$$

In today's experiment, you will compare your experimental value for the heat of a neutralization reaction to the value calculated from heats of formation.

Procedure

   A. Specific heat of a metal. Obtain a metal "shot" unknown from your instructor. Weigh out 30 g of the metal to at least the nearest 0.01 g (preferably 0.001 g) and transfer it to a clean, dry test tube. Clamp the test tube in a beaker of water mounted over a Bunsen burner with the top of the test tube at least 5 cm above the water level. Heat the beaker to boiling and then maintain it there for at least five minutes and until you are ready for the next part.

   Using a pipet or buret deliver 25.00 mL of water into a polystyrene cup. Insert and carefully read a thermometer every 0.25 minutes (15 seconds) for 1.75 minutes. At precisely the 2 minute mark, quickly transfer the heated metal to the cup being sure to stir immediately after transferring. Starting at the 2.25 minute mark, record the thermometer reading every 0.25 minutes for about three minutes. Be sure that the metal is properly recycled. If time is available, perform a second run.

   You are now ready to graphically determine the temperature change for the process. Graph the temperature on the vertical axis and the time on the horizontal axis. The data prior to mixing and subsequent to mixing are extrapolated using straight lines **to the time of mixing**. The temperature difference between the extrapolated lines at the time of mixing is the temperature change. Refer to *Figure 12-1* for an example of the analysis. Note however, that the temperature change in *Figure 12-1* is much larger than the change you will obtain here (a few degrees). Use of a computer interfaced temperature probe can considerably facilitate this procedure.

   The specific heat of the metal can now be calculated from the following treatment. The sum of the energy changes for the process must be zero or the energy gained by the water plus the energy lost by the heated metal must equal zero.

Let: m_w =   mass of water $m_w C_w \Delta t_w + m_u C_u \Delta t_u = 0$
       C_w =   specific heat of water
       Δt_w =   change of temperature of water

       m_u =   mass of unknown metal $C_u = -\dfrac{m_w C_w \Delta t_w}{m_u \Delta t_u}$
       C_u =   specific heat of unknown
       Δt_u =   change of temperature of unknown

   In 1819, it was observed by Dulong and Petit that for most metallic elements, the product of the atomic mass and the specific heat is close to the value 25 J/mol deg. Theoretical equations indicate that the value should be 3 times the gas law constant (8.313 J/mol deg) or 24.9 J/mol deg. We notice that theory and the early experimental results agree quite closely. By assuming the relationship, (atomic mass)(specific heat) = 25 J/mol deg [$(M_m)(C_p) = 25$], you can calculate an approximate atomic mass of your unknown and hopefully identify it.

   B. Heats of solution. When an ionic compound dissolves in water, energy is required to break up the crystal lattice (the attraction between ions is called the crystal lattice energy) but energy is released by the formation of bonds between ions and water (energy of hydration). When the energy of hydration is greater than the crystal lattice energy, the dissolving process will be exothermic and causes a temperature increase. When the crystal lattice energy exceeds the energy of hydration, the dissolving process is endothermic and the temperature of the system will drop (You should ask why it dissolves when the process is endothermic - see *Experiments 25* and *26* on the other part of the energy balance - entropy).

The temperature change upon dissolving of two different ionic compounds will be measured to determine the relative magnitudes of the crystal lattice energy and the heat of hydration. As calculations will not be performed on this part of the experiment, only approximate temperature changes will be determined.

1. Add 3 grams of lithium chloride to a dry test tube. Measure the temperature of 15 mL of water and transfer it to the tube. Thoroughly mix to dissolve the solid and read the temperature.

2. Repeat the above with 3 grams of ammonium chloride.

   C. Enthalpy of neutralization. The endothermicity or exothermicity of several acid and base reactions will be determined by measuring the temperature change upon mixing. From the results of the series of mixtures, you will be able to evaluate the effects of the nature and concentration of the acids and bases on the enthalpy changes of the reaction.

   For run 1, weigh a clean, dry polystyrene cup to at least the nearest 0.01 g. Add 50.0 mL of 2.00 M HCl to the cup with a graduated cylinder. Add 50.0 mL of 2.02 M NaOH to a beaker. Insert a thermometer into the acid solution and read its temperature every 0.50 minutes for 2.5 minutes. We will assume that both solutions are at the same temperature since they have been sitting in containers in the lab for some time. At exactly the 3 minute mark, pour the sodium hydroxide solution into the acid solution and stir vigorously with the thermometer. Resume taking temperature readings at 0.50 minute intervals at the 3.5 minute mark until a trend is established (about 5 minutes). Weigh the cup and contents.

   Repeat the above procedure for runs 2, 3 and 4 substituting the appropriate solutions as indicated in the chart below.

run	first reagent (50 mL)	second reagent (50 mL)
1	2.00 M HCl	2.02 M NaOH
2	2.02 M NaOH	2.00 M HCl
3	2.00 M HNO$_3$	2.02 M NaOH
4	1.00 M HCl	2.02 M NaOH

Temperature is plotted as a function of time. The data prior to mixing and subsequent to mixing are extrapolated using straight lines. The temperature difference between the extrapolated lines at the time of mixing is the temperature change. Refer to *Figure 12-1* for an example of the analysis. Use of a computer interfaced temperature probe can considerably facilitate this procedure.

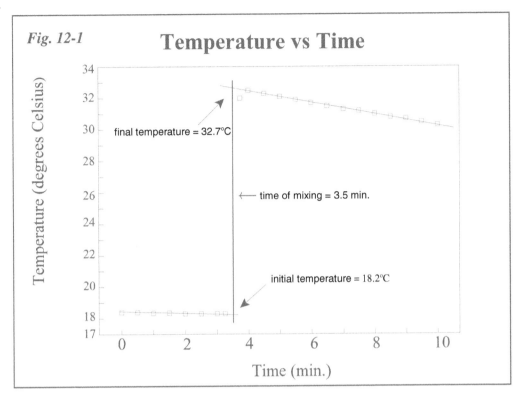

Fig. 12-1   **Temperature vs Time**

Graph the temperature on the vertical axis and the time on the horizontal axis. Extrapolate the data between 0 and 2.5 minutes using a straight edge to the 3.0 minute mark. Extrapolate the data between 3.5 and 9 minutes (or whenever you stopped) back to the 3.0 minute mark. Determine the temperature change between the two extrapolations at the 3.0 minute mark. Calculate the heat of neutralization and the molar heat of neutralization from the treatment that follows.

Let: ΔH_n = heat of neutralization
      $\underline{\Delta H_n}$ = molar heat of neutralization
      Δt = temperature change of solution
      m_s = mass of final solution
      C_s = specific heat of final solution
      a = number of moles of HCl

   $\Delta H_n + m_s C_s \Delta t$ $= 0$

         ΔH_n $= -m_s C_s \Delta t$

      $\underline{\Delta H_n}$ $= \Delta H_n / a$

Hess's law can be used to calculate the molar heat of neutralization from literature values for heats of formation of HCl, NaOH, NaCl and H_2O. These values and the specific heat needed for the calculations are in the table below.

$$\Delta H_r = \Sigma[n\Delta H_{f(products)}] - \Sigma[n\Delta H_{f(reactants)}]$$

solution	concentration (mol/L)	specific heat (J/g deg)	heat of formation (kJ/mol)
hydrochloric acid	1.00		-164.4
sodium hydroxide	1.00		-469.6
sodium chloride	1.00	3.90	-407.1
water			-285.9
nitric acid	1.00		-206.6
sodium nitrate	1.00	3.89	-446.2
0.5 M sodium chloride + 0.5 M sodium hydroxide		3.94*	

*estimated

D. Hess's law calculations using data available on the Internet. The *NIST* (National Institute of Standards and Technology) site on the Internet

http://webbook.nist.gov/chemistry/

can be used to obtain data for Hess's Law calculations. In this exercise, you will find the heats of formation of water (l and g) and carbon dioxide as well as the heats of formation and combustion for methane (g), ethane (g), propane (g), and 2,2,4-trimethylpentane (l). [Note: Commercially 2,2,4-trimethylpentane is called isooctane. The commercial name is not consistent with the naming system used by organic chemists but unfortunately finds common usage. Isooctane is one of the standards for determining the octane rating of gasoline. Its octane rating has arbitrarily been assigned a value of 100.] The heats of formation will be used to calculate the heats of combustion (using Hess's Law) for hydrogen, methane, ethane, propane, and 2,2,4-trimethylpentane (l) and the heat of vaporization of water. The calculated values for the hydrocarbons will be compared to the heats of combustion given at the *NIST* site.

Name_____Date_____Lab Section_____

Prelaboratory Problems - *Experiment 12* - Thermochemistry
The solutions to the starred problems are in *Appendix 4*.

1. The temperature change determined graphically is the difference in temperatures at the time of mixing. This is determined by extrapolating the data before and after mixing to the time of mixing.

    a. What does extrapolation mean?

    b.* Determine the temperature change in *Figure 12-1*.   _____

2.* The addition of 15.00 g of an unknown metal at 100.0 °C to 25.00 g of water at 22.0 °C resulted in a final maximum temperature of the system of 27.5 °C. Calculate the specific heat of the metal and its approximate atomic mass (see Dulong and Petit method on page 135 and *Problem 3* below). Suggest a name for the unknown metal.

    specific heat   _____

    atomic mass   _____

    element   _____

3. The addition of 21.60 g of an unknown metal at 80.0 °C to 20.00 g of water at 21.0 °C resulted in a final maximum temperature of the system of 23.0 °C. Calculate the specific heat of the metal and its approximate atomic mass (see Dulong and Petit method on page 135. Suggest a name for the unknown metal.

    specific heat   _____

    atomic mass   _____

    element   _____

4. The Dulong and Petit empirical relationship for the product of atomic mass and specific heat, $(M_m)(C_p) = 25$, indicates that the specific heat is inversely proportional to the atomic mass or proportional to the number of moles of particles as with colligative properties.

    a. Using the data in *Appendix 1* for at least four metals, test the Dulong and Petit relationship. Is it accurate?

    b. For use of the equation with molecules rather than atoms, the number 25 should be multiplied by the number of atoms per molecule. Is the value 4.184 joules/g deg. for water consistent with this oversimplified approach? Explain your answer (Note that there is a threshold temperature below which this approach will have significant error).

    c. Compared to metals, what two factors cause the specific heat of water to appear to be exceptionally high?

    _____   _____

    d. Does this concept work on other substances such as sodium chloride, potassium chloride, calcium chloride, aluminum chloride, carbon tetrachloride or methanol (CH_3OH)? Explain your answer. (See *Appendix 1* for specific heat data)

5. The addition of 50 mL of 2.02 M NaOH to 50 mL of 2.00 M HNO_3 at 22.0°C resulted in a maximum temperature of 36.1°C with a total mass of the solution of 100.0 g. Calculate the molar heat of neutralization and compare it to the result calculated from Hess's law (refer to data on page 138).

    experimental ΔH_n _____

    calculated ΔH_n _____

Name_____Date_____Lab Section_____

Results and Discussion - *Experiment 12* - **Thermochemistry**

A. Specific heat of a metal (graph the data below on one of graph sheets that follows).

Time (min.)	Run 1		Run 2	
	Water Temp. (°C)	Mixture Temp. (°C)	Water Temp. (°C)	Mixture Temp. (°C)
0.00	_____		_____	
0.25	_____		_____	
0.50	_____		_____	
0.75	_____		_____	
1.00	_____		_____	
1.25	_____		_____	
1.50	_____		_____	
1.75	_____		_____	
2.00	**MIX**		**MIX**	
2.25		_____		_____
2.50		_____		_____
2.75		_____		_____
3.00		_____		_____
3.25		_____		_____
3.50		_____		_____
3.75		_____		_____
4.00		_____		_____
4.25		_____		_____
4.50		_____		_____
4.75		_____		_____
5.00		_____		_____

	Run 1	Run 2
1. Unknown number	_____	
2. Mass of metal	_____	_____
3. Volume of water	_____	_____
4. Initial temperature of water from graph of page 141 data (see *Fig. 12-1* for method of determining this value and value for #8)	_____	_____
5. Density of water (from *Handbook of Chemistry and Physics)*	_____	_____
6. Mass of water calculated from volume and density	_____	_____
7. Temperature of metal	_____	_____
8. Final temperature of system from graph of page 141 data	_____	_____
9. Specific heat of water	_____	_____
10. Δt_w	_____	_____
11. Δt_u	_____	_____
12. Energy gained by water	_____	_____
13. Specific heat of unknown metal	_____	_____
14. Average value of specific heat if two runs performed		_____
15. Atomic mass of unknown metal (Dulong and Petit method on page 135)		_____
16. Probable identity of unknown metal (in addition to atomic mass, use logic and consider other observations). **Explain your answer.**		_____

B. Heat of solution.

1. Temperature change when 3 grams of lithium chloride is added
   to 15 mL of water (indicate + or −)   _____

2. Temperature change when 3 grams of ammonium chloride is
   added to 15 mL of water (indicate + or −)   _____

3. Which is greater for ammonium chloride, the lattice energy or
   the hydration energy? Explain your answer.   _____

C. Enthalpy of neutralization. (Remember to weigh the empty, dry cup before starting. Graph the data below on one of graph sheets that follows.)

Run 1 (2.00 M HCl + 2.02 M NaOH)			Run 2 (2.02 M NaOH + 2.00 M HCl)		
Time (min.)	HCl(aq) Temp. (°C)	Mixture Temp. (°C)	Time (min.)	NaOH(aq) Temp. (°C)	Mixture Temp. (°C)
0.00	_____		0.00	_____	
0.50	_____		0.50	_____	
1.00	_____		1.00	_____	
1.50	_____		1.50	_____	
2.00	_____		2.00	_____	
2.50	_____		2.50	_____	
3.00	MIX			MIX	
3.50		_____	3.50		_____
4.00		_____	4.00		_____
4.50		_____	4.50		_____
5.00		_____	5.00		_____
5.50		_____	5.50		_____
6.00		_____	6.00		_____
6.50		_____	6.50		_____
7.00		_____	7.00		_____
7.50		_____	7.50		_____
8.00		_____	8.00		_____
8.50		_____	8.50		_____
9.00		_____	9.00		_____
9.50		_____	9.50		_____

Be sure to weigh the cup and its contents before disposing of it. On the accompanying pieces of graph paper, plot temperature on the vertical axis and time on the horizontal axis. Following *Figure 12-1*, use a straight edge to draw the best straight line through the data prior to mixing and subsequent to mixing and extrapolate both to the 3.0 minute mark. Determine the temperature difference between the lines at the 3.0 minute mark and enter the data on page 145.

(Remember to weigh the empty, dry cup before starting. Graph the data below on one of graph sheets that follows)

Run 3 (2.00 M HNO₃ + 2.02 M NaOH)			Run 4 (1.00 M HCl + 2.02 M NaOH)		
Time (min.)	HNO₃(aq) Temp. (°C)	Mixture Temp. (°C)	Time (min.)	HCl(aq) Temp. (°C)	Mixture Temp. (°C)
0.00	_____		0.00	_____	
0.50	_____		0.50	_____	
1.00	_____		1.00	_____	
1.50	_____		1.50	_____	
2.00	_____		2.00	_____	
2.50	_____		2.50	_____	
3.00		MIX			MIX
3.50		_____	3.50		_____
4.00		_____	4.00		_____
4.50		_____	4.50		_____
5.00		_____	5.00		_____
5.50		_____	5.50		_____
6.00		_____	6.00		_____
6.50		_____	6.50		_____
7.00		_____	7.00		_____
7.50		_____	7.50		_____
8.00		_____	8.00		_____
8.50		_____	8.50		_____
9.00		_____	9.00		_____
9.50		_____	9.50		_____

Be sure to weigh the cup and its contents before disposing of it. On the accompanying pieces of graph paper, plot temperature on the vertical axis and time on the horizontal axis. Following *Figure 12-1*, use a straight edge to draw the best straight line through the data prior to mixing and subsequent to mixing and extrapolate both to the 3.0 minute mark. Determine the temperature difference between the lines at the 3.0 minute mark and enter the data on page 145.

	run 1	run 2	run 3	run 4
1st cup - 50 mL of:	2 M HCl	2 M NaOH	2 M HNO$_3$	1 M HCl
beaker - 50 mL of:	2 M NaOH	2 M HCl	2 M NaOH	2 M NaOH
1. Mass of empty polystyrene cup	_____	_____	_____	_____
2. Mass of cup + mixture	_____	_____	_____	_____
3. Mass of mixture	_____	_____	_____	_____
4. Initial temp. of 1st reagent (see *Fig. 12-1*, from extrapolation forward to 3.00 min.)	_____	_____	_____	_____
5. Final temp. of mixture (see *Fig. 12-1*, from extrapolation back to 3.00 min.)	_____	_____	_____	_____
6. Temperature change (Δt)	_____	_____	_____	_____
7. Total heat evolved in reaction (ΔH_n)	_____	_____	_____	_____
8. Number of moles of H_2O formed	_____	_____	_____	_____
9. Molar heat of neutralization ($\underline{\Delta H_n}$)	_____	_____	_____	_____
10. Molar heat of neutralization calculated from Hess's law and data on page 138	_____	_____	_____	_____
11. Percentage difference between experimental and calculated values	_____	_____	_____	_____

12. Write net ionic equations for the reactions in runs 1-4.

#1

#2

#3

#4

13. Comparing runs 1 and 2, does the order of mixing have a
significant effect on the temperature change? Explain your answer.   _____

14. Comparing runs 1 and 3, does the nature of the acid have a
significant effect on the temperature change? If not, why not?   _____

15. Compare values for runs 1 and 4 and explain any differences.

D. Hess's law calculations using data available on the Internet.

This exercise should be performed using the Internet site: http://webbook.nist.gov/chemistry/
After writing balanced equations for the combustion reactions listed below, locate a computer with
Internet access and enter the *NIST* site above. At this site, click on Name and then enter the name
of the compound of interest in the box. For carbon dioxide, water, methane, ethane and propane,
click on gas phase thermochemistry data and scroll down and find the standard heats of formation
data [$\Delta_f H_{gas}$]. and fill in the data in the table below. For water and 2,2,4-trimethylpentane, select
 Condensed phase thermochemistry and record the standard heats of formation [$\Delta H_{f\ liquid}$]. For
methane, ethane, propane and 2,2,4-trimethylpentane, you should also select   Reaction
thermochemistry data and record the top value [ΔH_c]. To make sure you are in the right place, the
value for methane is -890.7 kJ/mol.

1.   Write the reactions for the combustion of hydrogen, methane, ethane, propane and 2,2,4-
        trimethylpentane.

   a. $H_2(g)$ + $O_2(g)$ =

   b. $CH_4(g)$ + $O_2(g)$ =

   c. $C_2H_6(g)$ + $O_2(g)$ =

   d. $C_3H_8(g)$ + $O_2(g)$ =

   e. $C_8H_{18}(l)$ + $O_2(g)$ =

2.   Table of data and Hess's law calculation results

substance	$\Delta H_{f}^{\circ}{}_{gas}$ (kJ/mol)	$\Delta H_{f}^{\circ}{}_{liquid}$ (kJ/mol)	ΔH_{c}° (calculated) (kJ/mol)	ΔH_{c}° (from *NIST*) (kJ/mol)
carbon dioxide		na	na	na
water			na	na
methane		na		
ethane		na		
propane		na		
2,2,4-trimethylpentane				(from liquid)

3.   Which of the potential fuels, hydrogen, methane, ethane, propane, 2,2,4-trimethylpentane is the most efficient? Explain your answer.

4.   From the values for the heats of formation of liquid and gas phase water, calculate the heat for the phase change of liquid water to gas.

_____

5.   The value for the heat of vaporization of water is -40.7 kJ/mole. Can you account for any difference between the value calculated in #4 and the value of -40.7 kJ/mole?

6.   Suggest any methods you can think of to improve any part(s) of this experiment.

7.   Some of the *Learning Objectives* of this experiment are listed on the first page of this experiment. Did you achieve the *Learning Objectives*? Explain your answer.

11

SPECTROSCOPY OF COBALT(II) ION

Learning Objectives

Upon completion of this experiment, students will have experienced:
1. Preparation of a standard solution.
2. Quantitative dilutions.
3. Use of a spectrometer to determine an absorption spectrum and a Beer's law plot.

Text Topics

Quantitative dilutions, spectroscopy, Beer's law (for text correlations, see page ix).

Notes to Students and Instructor

This experiment should take about two hours.

Discussion

Can you imagine the world without color? Have you thought about how you are able to perceive color? The fact that colors are distinguishable suggests that information may be obtained from color determinations. Chemists use spectra for the analysis of composition, structure and concentration. Studies of spectra also led to the development of our current theory of the electronic structure of atoms and molecules. The observation that energetically excited atoms emit light of specific wavelengths that are unique for each element led Bohr, Schrodinger, and others to formulate our present day quantum theory of electronic orbitals.

Organic chemists routinely use infrared and nuclear magnetic resonance spectroscopy to provide important puzzle pieces for the determination of the structures of compounds. Analytical chemists utilize the relationship that the amount of light of a specific wavelength absorbed is proportional to the concentration of the absorbing species (Beer's Law: $A = \epsilon bc$ where A is the absorbtion, ϵ a proportionality constant that is determined by the nature of the absorbing species, b is the path length of light through the sample and c is the molarity of the absorbing species).

In our investigation today, visible light will be used to determine the value of the product ϵb for cobalt(II) solutions. Then Beer's law is used to determine the molarity of the cobalt(II) ion in a solution of unknown concentration. In round tubes of the same diameter, b is constant, but its value can only be approximated so it is better to simply determine the product of the two constants, ϵ and b than to try to determine them individually.

The visible and ultraviolet regions are only a small portion of the electromagnetic radiation spectrum but they encompass the region of energy necessary to promote electrons from ground state orbitals to higher energy orbitals. Considering the wave characteristics of light, its energy as you might have intuitively expected is directly proportional to its frequency, $E = h\nu$. Since the speed of light is the product of its wavelength and frequency, $c = \lambda\nu$, the energy is inversely proportional to the wavelength, $E = hc/\lambda$. It is important to recognize that the longer the wavelength, the lower the energy. Gamma rays, x-rays and ultraviolet radiation have shorter wavelengths and higher energy than visible light. Infrared, radio and TV have longer wavelengths and lower energy than visible.

Procedure

Preparation of solutions. Prepare 50 mL of a stock solution of 0.150 M cobalt nitrate by dissolving the appropriate amount of $Co(NO_3)_2 \cdot 6H_2O$ in 25 mL of deionized water in a small beaker. Transfer the solution to a 50 mL volumetric flask. Be sure to rinse the beaker and add the washings to the flask. Dilute to the mark and **thoroughly mix**.

Rinse a 25 or 50 mL buret with the cobalt(II) solution and then fill the buret. Clean, dry and number 0 - 5, six 13 x 100 mm test tubes or better yet colorimetry cuvettes. Deliver with the buret, 1.00 mL into test tube 1, 2.00 mL into test tube 2 and so on. Rinse the buret several times with deionized water and fill it with deionized water. Deliver 5 mL of deionized water into test tube 0, 4.00 mL into test tube 1 and so on. Check by eye to see that there is now a total of 5 mL in each test tube. **Thoroughly mix the contents of each test tube.** Obtain a cobalt nitrate solution of unknown concentration from your instructor.

Absorption spectrum. Before you perform the concentration study, it is first necessary to determine the absorption spectrum of cobalt(II) ion. The spectrum will be determined using only tube 5 and tube 0 for a blank. The other tubes would give identical absorption profiles with proportionally lower absorption values. The spectrum enables you to select the best wavelength for the concentration study. Familiarize yourself with the appropriate spectrometer instructions. For a *Spectronic 20*, set the wavelength to 430 nm (see *Figure 14-1* on page 167). With nothing in the sample compartment, set the left knob so that the transmission reads zero (when the sample compartment is empty, the light is mechanically blocked from reaching the detector therefore the amount of light transmitted is zero). In theory this setting of the left knob should not depend on the wavelength and should not have to be reset. It is wise to recheck it occasionally however. Now insert the water blank (tube 0) and calibrate the instrument by setting the right hand knob so that the instrument reads 100% transmission or 0.00 absorption. Insert tube 5 and record the absorption reading. Remove tube 5, change the wavelength to 460 nm and recalibrate the right hand knob with tube 0. [Note: Every time the wavelength is reset, the right knob of the instrument must be reset with a blank. For readings of different samples at the same wavelength, resetting is not required or recommended.] Insert tube 5 and read the absorption. Repeat the above process at 480 nm, 500 nm, 510 nm, 520 nm, 540 nm, 570 nm and 610 nm. Plot the absorption (y axis) vs the wavelength (x axis) and determine the wavelength of maximum absorption.

Beer's law Plot. Set the wavelength to the optimum wavelength determined immediately above and recalibrate the instrument. Successively insert tubes 1 - 5 and the unknown and record the absorption values. Plot the absorption (y axis) versus the concentration of cobalt(II) ion (x axis) and determine the concentration of the cobalt(II) ion in the unknown.

Name_____Date_____Lab Section_____

Prelaboratory Problems - *Experiment 14* - Spectroscopy of Cobalt(II) Ion
The solutions to the starred problems are in *Appendix 4*.

1.* The microwave oven in your house uses electromagnetic radiation that has a wavelength about 0.01 cm. The wavelength range of visible light is 400 - 700 nm. Which is more energetic, microwave or visible light and is it appropriate to say that a microwave "nukes" the food? Explain your answer.

2. a.* How many grams of $CuSO_4 \cdot 5H_2O$ are needed to prepare 50.0 mL of a 0.30 M $CuSO_4$ solution?

_____

   b.* If 2.00 mL of the 0.30 M $CuSO_4$ solution is diluted to 5.00 mL with water, what is the resulting $CuSO_4$ concentration?

_____

3. a. How many grams of $NiSO_4 \cdot 6H_2O$ are needed to prepare 200×10^2 mL of a 3.5×10^{-2} M $NiSO_4$ solution?

_____

   b. If 15.0 mL of the 3.5×10^{-2} M $NiSO_4$ solution is diluted to 50.0 mL with water, what is the resulting $NiSO_4$ concentration?

_____

4. a.* The light transmission ($-\log_{10}T = A = \epsilon bc$) at 600 nm of a 0.25 M $CuSO_4$ solution on a shoulder of its absorption peak is 59% in a 1.00 cm cell. What is the value of ϵ for $CuSO_4$ at 600 nm?

b.   The absorption values for 1 mm of pyrex at 320 nm and 280 nm are 0.15 and 1.3 respectively. What are the percent transmissions for 1 mm of Pyrex at these wavelengths?

c.   Would cells made out of Pyrex be useful for obtaining ultraviolet spectra below 270 nm? Explain your answer.

5.* In this experiment, you will prepare two graphs. The first will be absorption vs wavelength and the second, absorption vs concentration. Should either (or both) graph result in a straight line? Explain your answer.

6.   At a wavelength of 270 nm, a 0.040 M solution of acetone in water has an absorption of 0.64 in a 1.00 cm cell. The absorption of a solution of unknown concentration of acetone in water was 0.48 at the same wavelength and in the same cell. What is the concentration of acetone in the unknown? (Assume that there is zero absorption of light by water at 270 nm.)

7.   Can visible light cause excitation of an electron in water? Explain your answer.

Name_____Date_____Lab Section_____

Results and Discussion - *Experiment 14* - **Spectroscopy of Cobalt(II) Ion**

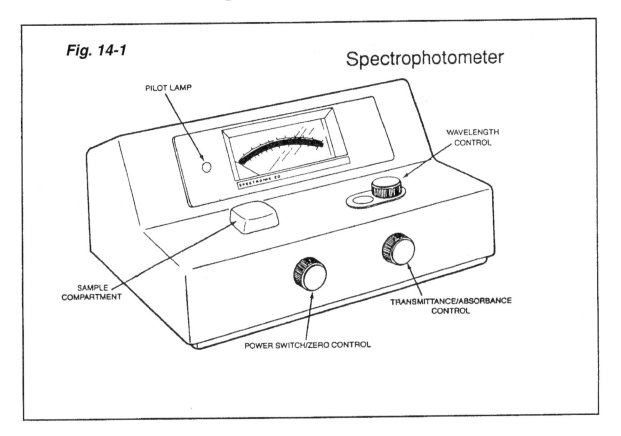

1. Formula mass of $Co(NO_3)_2 \cdot 6H_2O$ _____

2. Mass needed to prepare 50 mL of 0.150 M $Co(NO_3)_2$ _____

3. Mass of beaker + $Co(NO_3)_2 \cdot 6H_2O$ _____

4. Mass of beaker _____

5. Mass of $Co(NO_3)_2 \cdot 6H_2O$ _____

6. Moles of $Co(NO_3)_2 \cdot 6H_2O$ _____

7. Molarity of $Co(NO_3)_2$ _____

8. Absorption spectrum of tube 5

wavelength (nm)	absorption	wavelength (nm)	absorption
430	_____	520	_____
460	_____	540	_____
480	_____	570	_____
500	_____	610	_____
510	_____		

Graph A (y axis) vs λ and determine the optimum wavelength.
Explain your selection.   _____

9. Unknown identification number   _____

10. Beer's Law Plot

Tube #	Concentration (moles/L)	Absorption	Tube #	Concentration (moles/L)	Absorption
1	_____	_____	4	_____	_____
2	_____	_____	5	_____	_____
3	_____	_____	**unknown**		_____

11. Graph A (y axis) vs c (x axis) and determine the product ϵb from
    the slope of the line.   _____

12. Concentration of cobalt(II) read directly from graph.   _____

13. Concentration of cobalt(II) calculated using ϵb. Show calculations.   _____

14. Was Beer's Law obeyed? Explain your answer.   _____

15. Some of the *Learning Objectives* of this experiment are listed on the first page of this
    experiment. Did you achieve the *Learning Objectives*? Explain your answer.

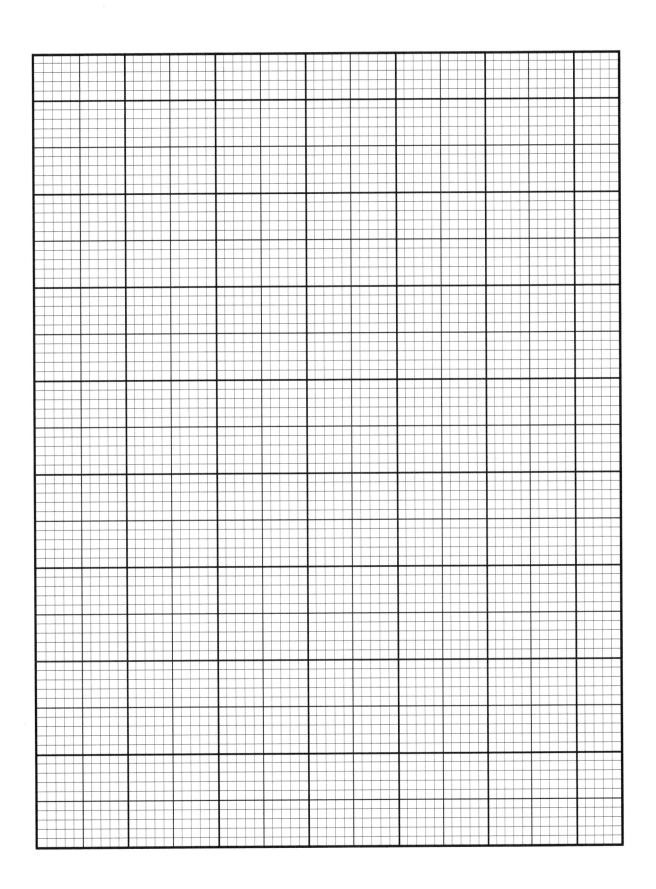

Name_____Date_____Lab Section_____

Postlaboratory Problems - *Experiment 14* - Spectroscopy of Cobalt(II) Ion

1. List some criteria that you think were used for the selection of cobalt(II) for this experiment.

2. Are there limitations to the concentrations of cobalt(II) ion that can be determined using this technique? Explain your answer.

3. List several additional cations and anions that you think could be analyzed quantitatively by visible spectroscopy.

4. Could visible spectroscopy be used for qualitative analysis of the ions you have listed in *#3*? If so, explain how.

5. In **Experiment 7**, copper(II) ion was quantitatively analyzed by a precipitation technique. Could visible spectroscopy have been used instead? If so, what criteria would you use to choose between the two techniques?

6. The method used to prepare the diluted concentrations of cobalt(II) solutions was not a technically correct method for preparing diluted solutions. The method was used here because of ease and to minimize the need for expensive glassware. What was not technically correct about the method and how should the dilutions have been performed?

7. Suggest any way you can think of to improve any part(s) of this experiment?

12

LEWIS STRUCTURES AND MOLECULAR MODELS

acetic acid

Learning Objectives

Upon completion of this experiment, students will have experienced:
1. Drawing Lewis structures of simple molecules and polyatomic ions.
2. Construction of models of simple molecules and polyatomic ions.

Text Topics

Lewis structures of molecules and polyatomic ions, (see page ix).

Notes to Students and Instructor

Students should work on Lewis structures before coming to the laboratory.

Discussion

Although it has recently become possible to image molecules and even atoms using a scanning tunneling microscope, most of our information about molecular structure comes from X-ray diffraction and interpretation of physical, chemical and spectroscopic properties of substances. This information often enables us to piece together a 3-dimensional picture or model of the molecule. On paper, one of the best methods we have of representing this model is by drawing a Lewis structure of the molecule or ion. The ability to draw Lewis structures for covalently bonded compounds and polyatomic ions is essential for the understanding of polarity, resonance structures, chemical reactivity and isomerism. Molecular models are useful tools to help you visualize the structures especially when the ion or molecule is not planar. It is not the intention here to teach you all aspects of the drawing of Lewis structures or the construction of molecular models but to guide you through some of the more fundamental aspects and provide a few clues where difficulty is often encountered.

Lewis structures. Remember the absolute rule that the Lewis structure <u>must show the correct number of electrons</u>. For a molecule, the sum of the valence electrons is the correct number. For an ion, it is the sum of the valence electrons and the negative of the charge on the ion. For example, formaldehyde, CH_2O, must show $4 + 2 + 6 = 12$ electrons and nitrite, NO_2^-, must show $5 + 6 + 6 + 1 = 18$ electrons. Then, whenever possible try to complete each atom's outer shell so that it has an octet (or duet for hydrogen) of electrons.

One general sequence to follow when constructing Lewis structures is:

1. Determine the correct number of electrons that must be showing (sum of the valence electrons and the negative of the charge on the ion).

2. Arrange the atoms in the correct sequence or sequences if there is more than one logical sequence. For polyatomic ions, the atom listed first (e.g. S in SO_4^{2-}) is usually the central atom (an atom attached to two or more atoms). For more information on choosing the correct sequence, see the discussion below.

3. Connect each of the atoms with a line or one bond.

4. Distribute the remaining electrons in pairs (subtract two each from the total for each bond already inserted) around the external atoms (the ones attached to the central atom) attempting to complete each atom's octet. Remember that the octet (duet for hydrogen) should never be exceeded for atoms through the second period and should only be exceeded for atoms beyond the second period when the atom is a central atom. If electrons still remain, attempt to fill the octets of central atoms or even exceed the octets for atoms beyond the second period.

5. If central atoms are short of achieving an octet, move electron pairs from external atoms to form multiple bonds between the external atom and the central atom in an attempt to provide all atoms with an octet (or, for atoms beyond the second period the octet might be exceeded).

6. If the total number of electrons is odd, it will be impossible to satisfy the octet rule for all atoms and in fact the species will be a free radical (it will have an unpaired electron) and probably will be a relatively reactive species.

7. Visually inspect the resulting structure and decide if it is consistent with other structures you have seen (generalities are difficult but the following are usually true):
    a. hydrogen has one bond
    b. carbon has four bonds (except for carbon monoxide, cyanide ion and unstable species)
    c. halogens have one bond unless the halogen is a central atom
    d. oxygen usually has two bonds except for polyatomic ions
    e. nitrogen usually has three bonds unless the nitrogen is the central atom

If the structure is not intuitively satisfying or if you cannot decide between different bonding sequences, determine the formal charge on each atom. You are probably familiar with the concept of oxidation number. Basically, the oxidation number method assumes that bonds are 100% ionic and assigns all the electrons in bonds to the more electronegative partner. For sodium chloride, this results in oxidation numbers of +1 for sodium and -1 for chloride. While this method gives a good model of the compound when the bonding is ionic, it should be considered nothing more than a bookkeeping method for covalent bonds. In other words, it is a useful method for determining if a reaction is a redox reaction and if so, what is oxidized and what is reduced. For covalent bonds, oxidation numbers give a very distorted view of the charges in the molecule. For instance, for HCl, the oxidation number method results in a +1 for hydrogen and -1 for chloride. In actuality, the hydrogen chlorine bond is best described as polar covalent with a partial positive charge on the hydrogen and a partial negative charge on the chlorine.

The formal charge method assumes that the bonds are 100% covalent with bonded electrons equally shared by the two partners. Thus the formal charge method gives an indication of the locations of charges in covalently bonded compounds. Although formal charges ignore differences in electronegativities, the method still provides useful information. In general, everything else being equal (e.g., octet rule is satisfied) **the structure with the minimum number of formal charges will be favored.** The formal charge is calculated from the following formula:

formal charge = valence electrons - bonds - nonbonded electrons

After you have determined the formal charges, choose the structure with the minimum number of formal charges. For some structures with central atoms that are beyond the second period (commonly phosphorous, sulfur, chlorine, bromine, iodine), it is sometimes preferable to move electrons from external atoms to form multiple bonds with the central atom. Apparently minimizing formal charge is energetically better than maintaining an octet for these atoms.

8. If it is possible to draw more than one reasonable structure by moving electrons only, then all of these structures should be drawn and connected by double headed arrows. These structures are resonance structures and the actual structure is a hybrid of all of the resonance structures. It is very important to realize that the actual structure is not going back and forth between the resonance structures but is a hybrid of the structures. For instance, if formal charges are different from one structure to the other, the formal charges on each atom are probably best represented by an average of the values in each structure.

9. Consider the geometry of the structure by applying VSEPR theory or a hybridization model to the resulting Lewis structure. Both models, when appropriately used will predict with very few exceptions the same shape. The table below summarizes the theories.

groups[1] of electrons around central atom	electronic shape[2]	bond angles	hybridization
2	linear	180°	sp
3	planar	120°	sp^2
4	tetrahedral	109.47°	sp^3
5	trigonal bipyramid	90°, 120°, 180°	dsp^3
6	octrahedral	90°, 180°	d^2sp^3

[1]The number of groups of electrons is equal to the sum of the number of neighbor atoms and nonbonded electron pairs.
[2]Be sure to distinguish electronic shape from molecular shape. If one or more of the groups of electrons are nonbonded pairs, the molecule needs to be described by the relative positions of the atoms; not by the shapes of the electronic orbitals.

For those of you who still want further help on drawing Lewis structures, one technique that can help is to determine the value of the expression $\pi_b = (6n + 2 - \#)/2$ where n is the number of atoms (not counting hydrogens) and $\# =$ the number of available electrons. If π_b is a positive whole number, it usually represents the number of extra or π bonds in the species. If π_b contains a fraction, the species will have an unpaired electron (a free radical) and not all atoms will have an octet. If π_b is negative, the species has as atom that exceeds the octet. For most examples in this course, π_b will be either zero or a positive number. When it is zero, all atoms are connected by single bonds. When the value is above zero, the value usually represents the number of π bonds that need to be included and this can save considerable time.

To illustrate the use of the preceding guidelines, the procedure will be applied to a couple of examples. Consider the molecule formaldehyde, CH_2O. First, determine the correct number of electrons that should show in the final structure which is $4 + 2 + 6 = 12$. Now we must consider the sequence of bonding. Three possible choices are (other possibilities can be eliminated because they require two bonds to hydrogen which except for some unusual boron compounds should be absolutely avoided):

$$\begin{array}{ccc} & C & O \\ H\,C\,O\,H & H\,O\,H & H\,C\,H \end{array}$$

As symmetrical choices are often favored, the first structure could be eliminated because it has lower symmetry than the other two. We will leave it in for this discussion and continue by inserting the three single bonds (6 e$^-$) and adding the remaining 6 e$^-$ to the external atoms (C and O respectively for the second and third structures) or 6 e$^-$ to the C and O of the first structure. To satisfy the octet rule in each structure, one nonbonded electron pair is moved from the external atom in the second and third structure to form a double bond with the central atom. For the first structure, the second nonbonded electron pair on either the C or O is moved between the two atoms to form a double bond.

Alternatively, the equation $\pi_b = (6n + 2 - \#)/2$ could be used to provide useful information before the electrons are inserted. For formaldehyde, π_b has the value $1 \rightarrow [(6)(2) + 2 - 12]/2$ (remember not to count hydrogens). This means that formaldehyde has 1 π bond. Why do this? Once you gain experience, you will simply write down the number of elements and fill in the total number of electrons while satisfying the duet and octet rules. But to begin with, this technique enables you to ascertain the right number of bonds and avoid some random guessing.

$$H - \overset{\cdot\cdot}{\underset{-1}{C}} = \overset{\cdot\cdot}{\underset{+1}{O}} - H \qquad \qquad \overset{:\overset{\cdot\cdot}{C}\ ^{-2}}{\underset{\underset{+2}{H - O - H}}{\|}} \qquad \qquad \overset{:\overset{\cdot\cdot}{O}}{\underset{H - C - H}{\|}}$$

The three structures are technically correct Lewis structures for CH_2O but only one correctly represents formaldehyde. In addition to considering symmetry, it is possible to choose between structures by evaluating the formal charge on each atom in a structure. The minimization of formal charges for CH_2O enables us to strongly favor the third and correct structure.

To draw Lewis structures of ions, the procedure is similar but a modification is needed. In determining the correct number of electrons, the number of valence electrons should be added to the negative of the charge. If the ion has a negative charge, it has extra electrons that it has acquired from its partners. The following example will illustrate the technique for nitrite, NO_2^-. The correct number of electrons is $5 + 12 + 1 = 18$. Use of the symmetry guideline leads to the sequence ONO rather than OON and in addition, a formal charge analysis on the completed Lewis structures (try it!) also favors ONO. Calculation of π_b yields a value of 1 indicating the presence of 1 π bond. By following the guidelines on page 174 and/or using the value of π_b, you should end up with the structures below. In this case, you should draw two structures that differ by the position of electrons only and are resonance structures. The double headed arrow below is the convention used to indicate that the two Lewis structures are resonance structures.

$$:\ddot{O}\!=\!\ddot{N}\!-\!\ddot{O}: \quad\longleftrightarrow\quad :\ddot{O}\!-\!N\!=\!\ddot{O}:$$
$${}_{-1}{}_{-1}$$

Remember that when resonance structures can be drawn, none of the Lewis structures correctly depicts the structure but one must try to imagine a hybrid (or enhanced average) as a better model for the species.

Now lets look at the geometry of formaldehyde and nitrite. For the formaldehyde molecule drawn earlier, there are 3 groups of electrons around the central carbon. Notice the double bond counts as 1 group of electrons and not 2! Focus on the shape around each atom and do not look at the oxygen when determining the shape around carbon. The 3 groups result in a prediction that the atoms around carbon are 120° apart in a plane.

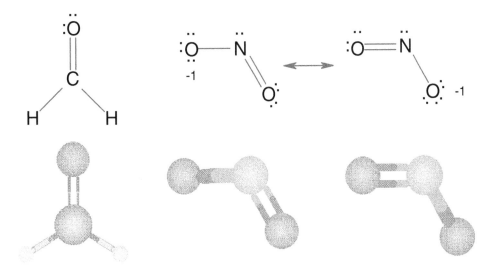

For nitrite, there are also 3 groups of electrons around the central nitrogen as the nonbonded electron pair counts as a group. Again VSEPR theory predicts 120° bond angles and a bent ion.

When 4 groups of electrons surround the central atom, a tetrahedral structure results which can be represented on paper as a projection. While projections are commonly used, CH_4 is often written in planar form with bond angles that appear to be $90°$. You should recognize when you see the planar drawing that the bond angles are actually $109.5°$ and that the molecule is tetrahedral.

Molecular polarity. Once the Lewis structure has been drawn and the geometry resolved, it is possible to determine if the molecule is polar. A knowledge of polarity is extremely useful for predicting relative boiling points, solubility, and chemical reactivity. For a molecule to be polar, it first must have polar covalent bonds and then it must have a geometry that does not result in the cancellation of bond dipoles. Except for carbon - hydrogen bonds, almost all bonds between different nonmetals are polar covalent. Thus if a molecule contains two different nonmetals and lacks the symmetry necessary for cancellation of bond dipoles, the molecule will be polar. For the formaldehyde (CH_2O) structure above, the carbon - hydrogen bonds are nonpolar but the carbon - oxygen bond is polar with a partial positive charge on the carbon and a partial negative charge on the oxygen. This means that formaldehyde should be a polar molecule. For further discussion of molecular polarity, see *Experiment 16*.

Molecular models. Most molecular model kits will help you visualize the structures, especially for molecules that are three dimensional. However, the most common ball and stick models compromise correctness for ease when multiple bonds are present. For instance, for formaldehyde, the carbon used will have its holes in a tetrahedral arrangement and the H-C-H bond angle will come out $109.5°$ and the H-C-O bond angle $125.3°$ instead of correct bond angles of $120°$. Also, for most models kits, the double bond is made up of two identical bent bonds but the hybridization model used in most organic chemistry texts characterize the double bond as two different kinds of bonds; a σ bond and a π bond.

Procedure

Recognizing the discrepancies discussed above, draw Lewis structures and construct models for the molecules and polyatomic ions listed in the *Results and Discussion* section.

Prelaboratory Exercises - *Experiment 15* - Lewis Structures and Molecular Models

Try to do the Lewis structures on the following pages before coming to laboratory.

Name_____Date_____Lab Section_____

Results and Discussion - *Experiment 15* - Lewis Structures and Molecular Models

1. For each molecule in the chart below, draw a Lewis structure, construct a model, determine the bond angle(s), molecular polarity (P = polar, N = nonpolar) and the hybridization of the central atom.

Molecule	Lewis Structure	Bond Angle	Polarity	Hybridization
F_2		____		
N_2		____		
ICl		____		
CO_2		____	____	____ C
H_2O		____	____	____ O

Molecule	Lewis Structure	Bond Angle	Polarity	Hybridization
NH$_3$		_____	_____	_____ N
CH$_4$		_____	_____	_____ C
C$_2$H$_6$		_____ H-C-H _____ H-C-C	_____	_____ C
C$_2$H$_4$		_____ H-C-H _____ H-C-C	_____	_____ C
C$_2$H$_2$		_____	_____	_____ C
HCN		_____	_____	_____ C

2. For the molecules below, draw the two reasonable, structurally different, possible Lewis structures. Calculate and indicate values of nonzero formal charges. Based on formal charges, circle the preferred structure, construct a model of it and answer the questions on bond angles and hybridization.

Molecule	Lewis Structures	Bond Angle	Hybridization
CH_4O		_____ H-C-H	_____ C
		_____ H-C-O	_____ O
		_____ H-O-C	
N_2O		_____	

3. For each of the molecules below, draw the two reasonable resonance structures and indicate the nonzero formal charges that are present (if any) in each of the structures. For each, construct a model of one of the resonance structures. (Hint: sulfur and nitrogen are the central atoms respectively and the hydrogen in nitric acid is bonded to an oxygen.)

Molecule	Lewis Structures	Bond Angle	Hybridization
SO_2		_____	_____ S
HNO_3		_____ H-O-N	_____ N
		_____ O-N-O	

4.   For each polyatomic ion in the chart below, draw all the reasonable resonance structures, indicate nonzero formal charges and construct a model of one of the resonance structures of each ion. Determine the indicated bond angle(s).

Polyatomic Ion	Lewis Structures	Bond Angle
OH^-		
CN^-		
ClO_2^-		_____
ClO_3^-		_____
CO_3^{2-}		_____

Polyatomic Ion	Lewis Structures	Bond Angle
SO_3^{2-}		____
SCN^-		____
HCO_2^-		____ H-C-O
		____ O-C-O
NO_2^+		____

Problems 5-10 attempt to demonstrate the importance of Lewis structures. In addition to providing a view of the shape and polarity of the molecule, Lewis structures sometimes provide insight into chemical reactivity. When the Lewis structure indicates some unusual or undesirable characteristic such as high formal charges or unusual oxidation numbers, strained bond angles, unpaired electrons or lack of an octet, there is a strong possibility that the molecule will exhibit extraordinary behavior. Basically this exercise is designed to show you that you can apply your knowledge of chemistry to new situations and think like a chemist.

5. Ozone (O_3) is needed in the stratosphere to absorb (and filter out) potentially damaging ultraviolet light. However, in the lower atmosphere it is a dangerous pollutant as it is a very reactive form of oxygen and as a result, very toxic and destructive. Draw the two reasonable resonance structures (Hint: it is not a ring) and indicate the bond angle and the nonzero formal charges. Suggest a reason for its high reactivity.

6. The combustion of gasoline in a car cylinder generates gas at a high temperature that pushes the cylinder down and powers the car. Unfortunately, nitrogen and oxygen combine at the high temperature in the cylinder to produce some undesired nitrogen monoxide. After emission from the exhaust, the nitrogen monoxide is oxidized by oxygen to nitrogen dioxide. NO_2 is one of the brown colored gases present in L. A. smog and is a very dangerous pollutant because of its very high reactivity. NO_2 establishes an equilibrium with its dimer N_2O_4. Draw Lewis structures of nitrogen dioxide and its dimer, dinitrogen tetroxide.

$$2\ NO_2(g) \ \leftrightharpoons\ N_2O_4(g)$$

Suggest a reason for the high reactivity of NO_2 and its dimerization reaction.

7. Hydrogen peroxide (H_2O_2) is a reactive molecule, often used as an antiseptic and sometimes used for bleaching. Draw a Lewis structure for hydrogen peroxide. Calculate the oxidation number of oxygen in hydrogen peroxide and suggest a reason for its reactivity.

8. Use of an atomic orbital approach to bonding without adding modifications for electron promotion and hybridization leads to the naive conclusion that carbon atoms should combine with hydrogen atoms to give CH_2. Draw a Lewis structure for this result. CH_2 (usually called methylene or carbene) actually can be made as a transient species and plays a very important role in synthetic organic chemistry. It has been described as one of the most indiscriminate reagents in organic chemistry. For example, it reacts with ethylene (C_2H_4) to give cyclopropane (C_3H_6). Show this reaction using Lewis structures for reactants and products and suggest a reason for the very high reactivity of methylene.

9. Bromomethane (CH_3Br) reacts with hydroxide ion to give methanol (CH_4O - see *Problem 2*) and bromide ion. Show this reaction using Lewis structures and use an explanation involving polarity to give a reason for the site of attack of hydroxide on bromomethane.

10. Sodium borohydride ($NaBH_4$) and lithium aluminum hydride ($LiAlH_4$) are very useful reducing reagents in organic chemistry. They are commonly used to reduce carbonyl compounds (aldehydes and ketones) to alcohols [e.g., acetone (CH_3COCH_3) to isopropyl alcohol ($CH_3CHOHCH_3$)].

    a. Draw the Lewis structures of acetone and isopropyl alcohol.

    b. Draw the Lewis structures of the borohydride and aluminum hydride ions. Calculate the oxidation numbers (Hint: consider electronegativities in chart on page 189) of boron, aluminum and hydrogen and suggest a reason for the reducing capability of the two ions.

11. Suggest any ways you can think of to improve any part of this experiment.

12. Some of the *Learning Objectives* of this experiment are listed on the first page of this experiment. Did you achieve the *Learning Objectives*? Explain your answer.

13

MOLECULAR POLARITY AND CHROMATOGRAPHY

Learning Objectives

Upon completion of this experiment, students will have experienced:
1. Application of molecular polarity concepts.
2. The techniques of extraction, paper chromatography, and fabric dyeing.

Text Topics

Electronegativity, molecular polarity, intermolecular forces, extraction, chromatography (for correlation to some textbooks, see page ix).

Notes to Students and Instructor

This experiment can be completed in a reasonable amount of time with careful planning. The chromatograms should be started first and the miscibility and fabric dyeing performed while the chromatograms progress.

Discussion

In the liquid state, the molecules of a substance are adjacent to each other and attracted together by intermolecular attractions. For covalently bonded substances, the attractions are usually classified into three groupings: dispersion forces (or London forces), dipole-dipole attractions and a sub category of the latter, hydrogen bonds. In the gaseous state, molecules behave as though they are independent of each other and do not experience significant intermolecular attractions except at high pressure or very low temperature. To boil a liquid requires that sufficient energy be supplied to overcome the intermolecular attractions. The boiling point should and does generally correlate with the strength of intermolecular attractions.

Very briefly, London forces are temporarily induced polarizations that result from the approach of two molecules. The magnitude of these forces depends on the size and shape of the molecules. As polarization of electron clouds are of prime importance in this effect, it would be expected that the strength of the attractions should depend partially on the number of electrons. As the number of electrons correlates with the molecular mass, the boiling point would be expected to correlate with molecular mass if other parameters do not change.

Consider the boiling points of the hydrocarbons in *Table 16-1*. These compounds consist of carbon-carbon and carbon-hydrogen bonds only. The former are obviously non-polar covalent bonds and the latter are about as non-polar as possible for bonds between two different elements. Thus the boiling points exhibit a steady increase due to increasing London forces. The hydrocarbons in *Table 16-1* do not have significant dipoles or charge separations and are good models for comparison with other compounds. [Note that another consideration is that the average molecular velocity decreases as the molecular mass increases (at a given temperature). This factor also contributes to the tendency of boiling points to increase with molecular mass.]

Table 16-1

alkane	formula	boiling point (°C)
methane	CH_4	-161.7
ethane	C_2H_6	-88.6
propane	C_3H_8	-42.1
butane	C_4H_{10}	-0.5
pentane	C_5H_{12}	36.1
hexane	C_6H_{14}	68.7
heptane	C_7H_{16}	98.4
octane	C_8H_{18}	125.7

Table 16-2

CH_4	NH_3	H_2O	HF
-161.7	-33.4	100	19.5
SiH_4	PH_3	H_2S	HCl
-111.8	-87.4	-60.7	-85.0
GeH_4	AsH_3	H_2Se	HBr
-88.5	-55	-41.5	-67.0
SnH_4	SbH_3	H_2Te	HI
-52	-17.1	-2.2	-35.4

In this paragraph and in *Prelaboratory Problem 4*, the data in *Table 16-2* and *Fig. 16-1* will be considered. Going down the periods in Group 4 from CH_4 to SnH_4, there is a steady increase in boiling points. This increase is consistent with an increase in dispersion forces and lower average molecular velocities as the molecular mass increases. However, *Table 16-2* reveals two anomalies that deserve our attention. First, the compounds of the second period elements, C, N, O and F with H all have similar numbers of electrons thus dispersion forces should be similar. On this basis, the boiling points for CH_4, NH_3, H_2O and HF should be similar. Since the data contradict this prediction, another attraction must

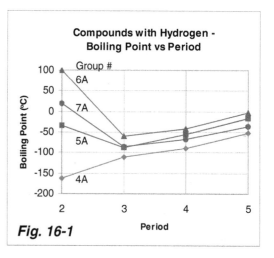

Fig. 16-1

come into play. This attraction is called hydrogen bonding. The second anomaly is apparent when we compare the boiling points of NH_3 with that of PH_3, H_2O with that of H_2S, HF with that of HCl. Despite the greater number of electrons of the second compound of each comparison, the first compound has a much higher boiling point. Hydrogen bonding again accounts for the apparent discrepancy. Hydrogens bonded to N, O and F are capable of hydrogen bonding to an N, O or F in another molecule. None of the other elements is electronegative enough to have this capability.

Another consequence of the increasing bond polarity going across the second period is that the non-polar methane (non-polar because of non-polar bonds and its high symmetry) is not soluble in the very polar water. However, methanol (CH_3OH) with polar carbon - oxygen and oxygen - hydrogen bonds and ammonia with polar nitrogen - hydrogen bonds are miscible with water. Methanol and ammonia both form strong hydrogen bonds with water.

Fig. 16-2

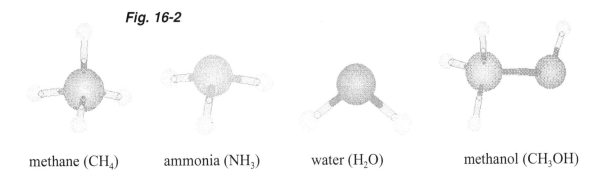

methane (CH_4)   ammonia (NH_3)   water (H_2O)   methanol (CH_3OH)

Intermolecular attractive forces and especially hydrogen bonds are extremely significant in chemistry. They influence boiling points, solubility, chemical reactivity and are responsible for determining the 3-D structures of proteins and DNA. Bond polarity can be predicted by an examination of Pauling's empirical values of electronegativities. One set of values for many elements are in the following chart: [Extracted from A. L. Allred, *J. Inorg. Nucl. Chem.*, 17, 215 (1961).]

Table 16-3

H = 2.20						
Li = 0.98	*Be = 1.57*	*B = 2.04*	*C = 2.55*	*N = 3.04*	*O = 3.44*	*F = 3.98*
Na = 0.93	*Mg = 1.31*	*Al = 1.61*	*Si = 1.90*	*P = 2.19*	*S = 2.58*	*Cl = 3.16*
K = 0.82	*Ca = 1.00*	*Ga = 1.81*	*Ge = 2.01*	*As = 2.18*	*Se = 2.55*	*Br = 2.96*
Rb = 0.82	*Sr = 0.95*	*In = 1.78*	*Sn = 1.96*	*Sb = 2.05*	*Te = 2.1*	*I = 2.66*

Generally, when the electronegativity difference between two bonding partners is very small (such as for the carbon-hydrogen bond), the bond behaves as though it is non-polar. As the electronegativity difference increases, the bond polarity increases to the limiting point where the bond is completely ionic. **It is easier to just remember that bonds between identical elements and the important carbon - hydrogen bond are non-polar while most other nonmetal - nonmetal bonds are polar covalent. Metal to nonmetal and metal to polyatomic ion bonds usually have predominantly ionic character.** For a molecule to be polar, there must be polar bonds and a lack of symmetry in structure such that the bond dipoles do not cancel each other out. CCl_4 has polar bonds but because of its tetrahedral geometry, is a non-polar molecule. Water has polar bonds and because of its bent geometry is highly polar. In general, polar molecules will have higher boiling points than non-polar molecules with similar molecular mass. Molecules with similar polarities will have a greater tendency to dissolve in each other or "like dissolves like."

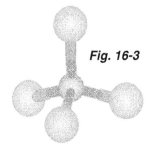

Fig. 16-3

The above considerations will be applied to miscibility tests, extraction experiments, dyeing of fabrics and paper chromatographic separations. You are aware that ethanol (CH_3CH_2OH) and water are miscible in all proportions (consider vodka - 40 to 50% ethanol). This is because both ethanol and water are polar molecules and due to *hydrogen bonding* are strongly attracted to each other. But what happens when the organic compound has no polar bonds such as in kerosene? We will investigate the miscibility of water and kerosene in this experiment.

Extraction. Consider an immiscible pair of liquids such as vinegar (polar - 95% water, 5% acetic acid) and oil (non-polar). Suppose the vinegar has a small amount of a non-polar solute dissolved in it and you shake the vinegar with some oil. The solute will have two options. As its polarity is closer to that of the oil than of vinegar, the solute will probably shift to the oil. We say that the solute has been extracted from the vinegar by the oil. If the solute had been polar, it would have remained in the vinegar.

Paper chromatography. Chromatography can be thought of as a dynamic extraction where the solute continually has an option of two phases. This is accomplished by having one phase move by a stationary phase. Chromatography was discovered by Michael Tswett (a Russian botanist) early in the 20th century. Tswett allowed a mixture of pigments extracted from plants to percolate down through a column of calcium carbonate. Solvent was added from the top as needed to cause continuous movement of the pigments down the column. Pigments that were more strongly attracted to the stationary phase (calcium carbonate) and had less affinity for the solvent (moving phase) moved down the column more slowly than pigments that had greater affinity for the solvent and had weaker attraction for the stationary phase. Tswett observed that the pigments had separated into several differently colored bands as a result of the fact that they moved down the column at different rates. The term chromatography was coined to describe the phenomenon.

The paper chromatography experiments you will perform today utilize the same principles Tswett employed. A piece of paper, spotted with pure compounds and mixtures is placed in a solvent as illustrated in *Figure 16-4*. Assume spots 1, 2, and 3 are pure compounds and spot 4 is an unknown mixture of the compounds. The solvent (moving phase) will move up the paper (stationary phase). When the solvent reaches the spots, the components of each spot have options. They can dissolve in the solvent and progress up the paper or they can stay adsorbed on the paper and resist movement. The preference depends on several factors including the polarities of the compounds, the solvent and the paper. The solvent and the stationary phase are selected so that the components spend some time in each phase and do not move right along with solvent front or stay at the origin. If the solvent and the stationary phase are selected properly, different compounds will move up the paper at different rates and separate.

The spots of compounds that are less strongly adsorbed on the paper will move up the paper faster than the spots of the more strongly adsorbed compounds. When the solvent front nears the top of the paper, the chromatogram is removed from the solvent and the solvent front marked with a pencil. To find out the composition of the fourth spot two factors are considered, color and relative distance moved. To quantify the relative distances, the R_f (ratio to front) value of each spot is calculated.

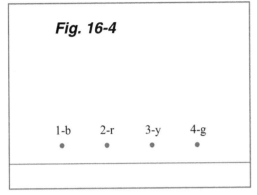

b = blue
r = red
y = yellow
g = green

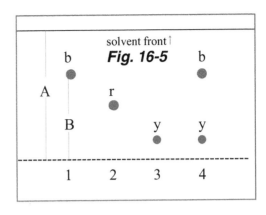

R_f = $\dfrac{\text{distance from origin to center of spot}}{\text{distance from origin to solvent front}}$ = $\dfrac{B}{A}$ for spot 1

In the chromatogram above, it can be seen that spot 4 (the green spot) has compounds with the same color and R_f values as pure compounds 1 and 3. This provides strong evidence (but not proof) that spot 4 contains compounds 1 and 3 and does not contain compound 2. Paper chromatography then serves as a separation technique and can also assist with identification if the possible compounds in a mixture are available in pure form.

Fabric dyeing. Many dyes used to color fabrics are polar molecules. Several different types of polymers are used to make fabrics; some have polar groups and others do not. Based on the principle "like dissolves like", polar dyes would be expected to stick to and color polar polymers and be rather ineffective dyes for non-polar fabrics.

Procedure

[Note: It is strongly recommended that you start Part C (paper chromatography) first and do the remaining parts while the chromatograms progress.]

A. Miscibility. Transfer the following liquids into test tubes and attempt to mix. Determine whether the mixtures are miscible or immiscible.

1. 5 mL water + 2 mL ethanol (CH_3CH_2OH)
2. 5 mL water + 2 mL kerosene (hydrocarbon with 10 to 16 carbons)

B. Extraction.

1. Consider the polarities of water and elemental iodine. Should iodine be very soluble in water? Visually inspect the stock solution of aqueous iodine. Can you tell if you were right? Look up the solubility of iodine in water in the *Handbook of Chemistry and Physics*. Do you think iodine should be very soluble in kerosene? Will the iodine prefer water or kerosene if you give the iodine the option? Decant 5 mL of the aqueous iodine solution into a test tube, add 2 mL of kerosene and shake vigorously. Record your observations.

2. Methylene blue is an ionic compound (and therefore polar) but it is a very large molecule and therefore has limited solubility in water. Will the methylene blue prefer water or kerosene? Pour 5 mL of the aqueous methylene blue solution into a test tube, add 2 mL of kerosene, stopper the tube and shake vigorously. Record your observations and conclusions.

   C. Paper chromatography. The same general procedure will be followed for your two chromatograms. Following *Figures 16-6* and *16-8*, draw straight pencil lines two centimeters from the bottoms of both pieces of chromatography paper and place pencil dots at equal intervals along the lines. Spot the larger paper with the felt-tip pens, as shown in the diagrams. The spots should be about this size ●.

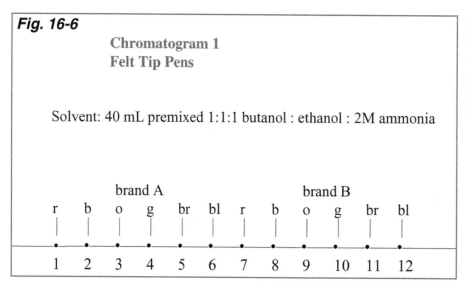

r-red
b-blue
o-optional
g-green
br-brown
bl-black

After the spotting (*Figure 16-6*) is complete, roll the paper into a cylinder and staple it so that there is a small gap between the two ends (*Figure 16-7*). The ends of the paper should **not** overlap. Add 40 mL of the butanol, ethanol, ammonia solvent to a 600 mL beaker. Gently put the paper cylinder (spotted edge down) into the beaker and cover the beaker with plastic wrap. Do not move or turn the beaker again until you remove the paper. At this point, you should begin your second chromatogram but keep your eye on the first one. When the solvent front reaches about 2 cm below the top of the paper, remove the chromatogram. Mark the solvent front with a pencil and dry the paper in the hood, with a hot air blower.

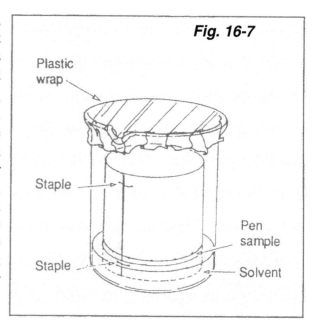

Following *Figure 16-8*, spot the smaller piece of paper with the metal ion solutions and with your unknown. To do this, draw some of the solution up into a capillary tube and apply it to the paper on the appropriate pencil dot. Again, the spots should be about this size, ●. Before spotting your chromatogram, practice your spotting techniques on a scrap piece of chromatography paper. Put 7 mL of 6 M hydrochloric acid and 25 mL of acetone into your 400 mL beaker and stir the mixture until the liquids are *thoroughly mixed*. Staple the paper into the form of a cylinder, as you did with the larger paper; gently place it into the 400 ml beaker and cover the beaker with the plastic wrap. When the solvent front reaches about 1 cm below the top of the paper, remove the paper from the beaker and mark the solvent front with a pencil.

1 - iron(III)
2 - copper(II)
3 - cobalt(II)
4 - manganese(II)
5 - mixture of 1,2,3,4
6 - unknown

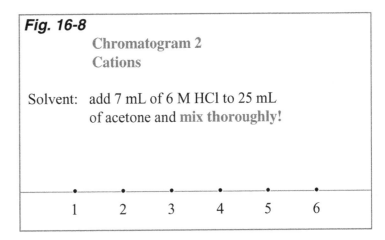

Fig. 16-8

Chromatogram 2
Cations

Solvent: add 7 mL of 6 M HCl to 25 mL
            of acetone and **mix thoroughly!**

1   2   3   4   5   6

Dry the metal ion chromatogram carefully with a hot air blower, outline and record colors of any spots that are visible, place it over a Petri dish __in the hood__ containing concentrated ammonia *[Caution: avoid touching the ammonia or breathing the vapors]* and cover with a watch glass for a few minutes until the spot labeled Mn^{2+} has appeared. Be sure to expose the entire chromatogram to the ammonia vapor. Outline any new spots that appear and record any changes in color in the matrix on page 200. Heat the chromatogram a second time with the hot air blower and again record any changes in spot color.

On both chromatograms, outline each of the spots with a pencil and measure the distance from the origin to the center of each spot. The distance from the origin to the center of the spot, divided by the distance form the origin to the solvent front (see *Figure 16-5*), is the R_f of the spot. Record the R_fs of all spots on your data sheet. Turn in your chromatograms with your report.

D. Fabric Dyeing. A company called *TESTFABRICS, INC.* (200 Blackford Ave., P.O. Box 420, Middlesex, New Jersey 08846) produces a product called "Multifiber Fabric 43" that you will use for this experiment (Alternatively *TESTFABRICS, INC.* also has a less expensive fabric with six different fabrics). Each 2" x 4" piece of this fabric contains 13 different fibers in ⅓" wide bands. The list and order of the fibers is given in the *Results and Discussion* section. Transfer 20 mL of an aqueous dye solution containing 0.05% eosin to a 50 mL beaker. Place the testfabric in the solution and heat it to boiling for about 5 minutes. Use tongs to remove the fabric from the bath, allow it to cool, wash it thoroughly with running water and set it aside for drying. Record the color of each fiber. Based on the knowledge that eosin is a polar dye, determine the relative polarities of each fiber.

Note: Other dye solutions (such as methyl orange) also work but most use dyes that are suspected carcinogens. For instructions on the preparation of other dyes for use in this experiment, see for example, Williamson, K. L., *Macroscale and Microscale Organic Experiments*, Heath, 614-620 (1989). Also *Testfabrics, Inc.*, (phone # 201 469-6446) sells identification stains that give many more colors and can be used to identify fabrics.

Chromatogram Summary

Description	Chromatogram 1 Felt-Tip Pens	Chromatogram 2 Cations
paper size	11 x 19.5 cm	9.5 x 14 cm
beaker size	600 mL	400 mL
solvent	40 mL premixed 1:1:1 1-butanol, ethanol, 2 M ammonia	prepare immediately before use - 7 mL of 6 M HCl + 25 mL acetone, mix thoroughly
distance between spots	1.5 cm	2.0 cm
distance of spots from bottom	2.0 cm	2.0 cm

spots		
	Brand A[1]	Cations
1	red	Fe^{3+}
2	blue	Cu^{2+}
3	optional	Co^{2+}
4	green	Mn^{2+}
5	brown	$Fe^{3+},Cu^{2+},Co^{2+},Mn^{2+}$
6	black	unknown
	Brand B[2]	
7	red	
8	blue	
9	optional	
10	green	
11	brown	
12	black	

visualization	dry (hot air blower)	a. dry with hot air blower b. place over Petri dish of concentrated NH_3 c. dry again
analysis	Report color, spot distance and R_f value for each pigment in every pen.	After each step (a,b,c), outline each spot and report its color. Determine all R_f values and identify cations in unknown.

[1] Flair or Paper Mate (same company) suggested
[2] Instructor's option

Name_____Date_____Lab Section_____

Prelaboratory Problems - *Experiment 16* - Molecular Polarity and Chromatography   The solutions to the starred problems are in *Appendix 4*.

1.   Which of the following would you expect to have a higher boiling point? Explain your answers.

   a.* CH_4 or HF

   b. CH_3OCH_3 or CH_3CH_2OH

   c. CH_4 or C_2H_6

   d.* CH_4 or SiH_4

2.   Should the first compound listed be more soluble in the first solvent or the second? Explain your answer.

   a.* NaCl in water or kerosene

   b. HCl in water or kerosene

   c. Wax in water or kerosene

3.   Calculate the R_f values for A, B and C in *Figure 16-9*. What are the components of mixture M?

R_f = ____ (A)

R_f = ____ (B)

R_f = ____ (C)

R_f = ____, ____ (M)

Components of M = _____

_____

Fig. 16-9

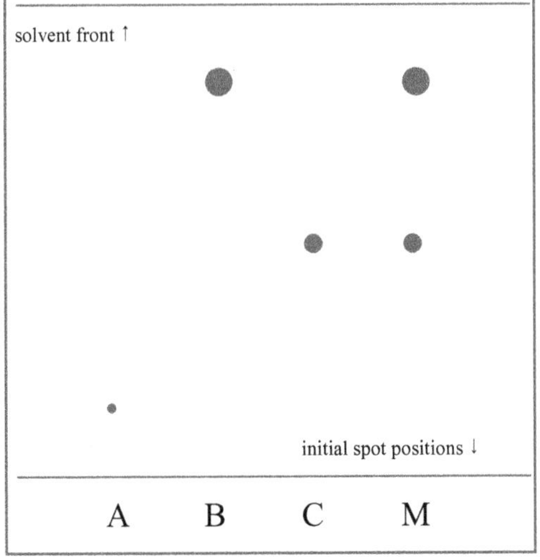

solvent front ↑

initial spot positions ↓

A   B   C   M

4. Please refer to *Tables 16-2*, *16-3* and *Figures 16-1* and *16-10* for these questions.

a. Briefly summarize the evidence that hydrogens intramolecularly bonded to N, O or F can form intermolecular hydrogen bonds to N, O or F.

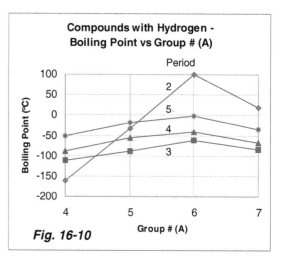

Fig. 16-10

b. Is there any evidence that chlorine forms hydrogen bonds? Explain your answer.

c. General guidelines for determining the nature of a bond from electronegativity scales are that the bond can be considered: ionic if the electronegativity difference between the bonded elements is greater than 1.7, polar covalent if the electronegativity difference is between 0.5 and 1.7 and non-polar covalent if the electronegativity difference is between 0 and 0.5. According to this guideline, bonds from carbon to sulfur and iodine should be non-polar covalent but you will find in organic chemistry that these bonds react as though they are polar covalent. That is why this text prefers the bold statement on page 189 for the determination of the nature of bond. Additionally, use of the bold statement has the advantage that it does not require access to an electronegativity table. Another apparent problem generated by the use of electronegativities is that chlorine is at least as electronegative as nitrogen. Explain how your answers to 4-a and 4-b above seem to be in conflict with the electronegativities of N and Cl.

Name_____Date_____Lab Section_____

Results and Discussion - *Experiment 16* - Molecular Polarity and Chromatography

A. Miscibility

mixture	Miscibility (M = miscible, I = immiscible)

1. water + ethanol   _____

2. water + kerosene   _____

B. Extraction

1. Should iodine be very soluble in water? Explain your answer.   _____

2. Solubility of iodine in water from *Handbook of Chemistry and Physics*. edition_____page_____   _____

3. Should iodine be very soluble in kerosene? Explain your answer.   _____

4. Observations when aqueous iodine and kerosene are mixed.

    Explanations and conclusions.

5. Observations when aqueous methylene blue and kerosene are mixed.

    Explanations and conclusions.

C. Paper chromatography

1. Chromatogram 1 - Ink Pigments

Brand A _____ Brand B_____ Origin to solvent front_____

pigments

	spot #		color	dist.	R_f	color	dist.	R_f	color	dist.	R_f	color	dist.	R_f
	1	red												
	2	blue												
	3	_____												
A	4	green												
	5	brown												
	6	black												
	7	red												
	8	blue												
	9	_____												
B	10	green												
	11	brown												
	12	black												

a. Evidence that two compounds are the same is provided when colors of spots from different sources match and R_f values are within experimental error of each other. Based on color and R_f value, some of the Brand A pigments are used in several different colored Brand A felt-tip pens. Give the color and R_f values of the pigments in the red, blue, optional and green pens that are also apparently used to make black ink.

		black				red			black			blue	
R_f	color				R_f	color			R_f	color			R_f	color
___	___				___	___			___	___			___	___
___	___				___	___			___	___			___	___

		black							black			green	
R_f	color				R_f	color			R_f	color			R_f	color
___	___				___	___			___	___			___	___
___	___				___	___			___	___			___	___

b. Which pigments, if any, are present in the brown and black Brand A pens and not present in any of the other Brand A pens? Give the color and R_f of any such pigments.

black pen _____ brown pen _____

c. Give the color and R_f values of any Brand A pigments that are the same as those used by Brand B.

Brand A pen color	R_f	common color	Brand B pen color	R_f
___	___	___	___	___
___	___	___	___	___
___	___	___	___	___
___	___	___	___	___
___	___	___	___	___
___	___	___	___	___
___	___	___	___	___
___	___	___	___	___

2. Chromatogram 2. Metal Ions

Unknown #_____   Origin to solvent front _____

solution #	ion	Color after drying	after ammonia	after 2nd dry	dist (cm.)	R_f	ion
1							
2							
3							
4							
5							
6 unknown	spot 1						
	spot 2						
	spot 3						
	spot 4						

D. Fabric Dyeing. Record the color of each fiber. Based on the color of each fiber, rate the relative polarity of the fiber on a scale of 1 to 5 with 1 being very polar and 5 non-polar.

Fiber	Color	Relative polarity
Acetate (bright Celanese staple)[1]	_____	_____
SEF (Monsanto Modacrylic)	_____	_____
Arnel (bright filament)	_____	_____
Cotton (bleached)[2]	_____	_____
Cresian 61	_____	_____
Dacron 54 Polyester[4]	_____	_____
Dacron 64 Polyester	_____	_____
Nylon 66[3]	_____	_____
Orlon 75 Polyester[5]	_____	_____
Silk	_____	_____
Polypropylene	_____	_____
Viscose	_____	_____
Worsted Wool[6]	_____	_____

[1-6]The fabrics given with superscripts are listed in the order that they appear in the six fabric sample.

Name_____Date_____Lab Section_____

Postlaboratory Problems - *Experiment 16* - **Molecular Polarity and Chromatography**

1. Solubility tests are often used to help distinguish and identify ionic compounds (see for example, *Experiment 9*). Solubility is sometimes also useful for the identification of organic compounds. After referring to *Appendix 1*, suggest a method for distinguishing between ethanol and cyclohexane.

2. Extraction is a technique that is commonly used to separate organic compounds from inorganic compounds as well as organic acids, bases and neutral compounds.

    a. Benzoic acid is soluble in ether. Suggest a step by step procedure for the separation of sodium chloride and benzoic acid.

    b. Could sodium chloride and potassium nitrate be separated using extraction? Explain your answer.

3. The most difficult part of the chromatography experiment was done by the scientists who selected the solvents for the separations. While a consideration of polarities is certainly used for selection of the stationary and moving phases, much of the work must be done by trial and error. If you were given the assignment of analyzing a mixture of organic non-polar pesticides using thin layer chromatography (paper chromatography is a specific type of thin layer chromatography - with thin layer chromatography there are additional choices for the stationary phase besides cellulose), would you start with a solvent with high polarity such as water? Explain your answer.

4. In addition to using paper chromatography as an identification technique, it is possible to cut out spots from the developed chromatogram and to extract the separated compounds into appropriate solvents. Thus the technique can serve as a separation and purification technique. Comment on limitations this method would have based on sample size.

5. Suggest any ways you can think of to improve any part of this experiment.

6. Some of the *Learning Objectives* of this experiment are listed on the first page of this experiment. Did you achieve the *Learning Objectives*? Explain your answer.

14

COOLING CURVES AND CRYSTAL STRUCTURES

Learning Objectives

Upon completion of this experiment, students will have experienced:
1. The use of cooling curves to determine melting points.
2. A study of the effects of impurities on melting points.
3. The determination of the atomic radius of a metal from its density.

Text Topics

Colligative properties, melting points and the effects of impurities on melting ranges, crystal structure, atomic radius (for correlation to some textbooks, see page ix).

Notes to Students and Instructor

The length of this experiment can be varied from 2 to 3 hours depending on the number of cooling curve trials on each sample. Lauric acid is suggested for use here for several reasons: it has a low tendency to supercool, it is not too expensive, and its melting point (around 43°C) means that 0 to 50°C thermometers can be used. If digital thermometers are available, myristic, palmitic and stearic acids are alternative choices and all four acids have the same freezing point depression constant. A computer interfaced temperature probe considerably facilitates this experiment.

Discussion

Cooling Curves. The capillary method of measuring melting ranges that was used to determine the success of your purification of vanillin (**Experiments 2 and 3**) is quick, accurate and uses small amounts of sample. Using the capillary method, you heated the sample and recorded the melting temperature range. Today you will do the reverse; heat the sample above the melting range and observe it while it cools and solidifies. Rather than simply recording the solidification range which is not easily observed, you will obtain data and graph a curve by recording the temperature of the cooling sample as a function of time. While this method is not quick or routine, it does provide information not readily available from the capillary method.

Ideally the temperature of the liquid sample should decrease at a steady rate until it reaches its freezing temperature, hold for some time while all of the sample solidifies and then cooling should resume at a steady rate as is illustrated in *Figure 18-1*. In practice, however, you may obtain curves that look more like *Figures 18-2 and 18-3*. Point *A* is due to supercooling of the liquid and can be avoided or at least minimized by continuous stirring of the sample during cooling. The slight slope at *B* is due to the presence of impurities. Recall from **Experiment 3** that impurities or additives depress melting points (why is salt put on roads in the winter and used with ice to make ice cream?). The changing slope near *C* or the slowing of the cooling rate is due to the approach to room temperature.

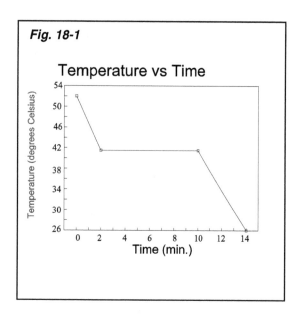

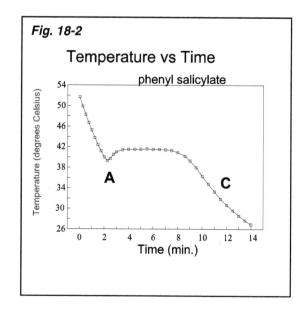

The melting point of the sample is obtained by drawing with a straight edge the best straight line through the steadily declining points of the liquid and another line through the slightly sloped "plateau". The intersection of the lines is taken as the melting point.

One of the advantages of the cooling curve method is that the amount of depression caused by impurities can be accurately determined. The freezing point depression is a useful parameter as it is a colligative property. This means that the amount of the depression is related simply to the number of moles of particles added and not to the nature of the particles. In other words one mole of acetone will depress the melting point of water the same amount as 1 mole of ethanol. As 1 mole of

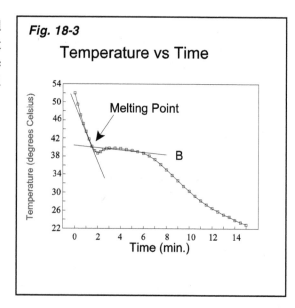

sodium chloride provides two moles of particles, it will depress the freezing point twice as much as one mole of acetone. Because it is a colligative property, it is possible to demonstrate that the freezing point depression is directly proportional to the number of moles of solute dissolved in a given amount of solvent. Because of the way samples are prepared and the nature of the relationship, concentrations are expressed in molality (moles of solute/kg of solvent).

$$\Delta t_f \ = \ k_f m \qquad (\Delta t = \text{temperature change in } {}^\circ C, \ k_f = \text{freezing point depression constant,}$$

m = molality of solute)

The freezing point depression constant, k_f is dependent on the nature of the solvent and must be experimentally determined for each solvent. If the constant is known and the amount of the freezing point depression is measured, the molality of the additive can be calculated. If the mass of the solute and solvents are measured, the molecular mass of the solute can be calculated. Thus freezing point depression measurements are a method for determining the molecular mass of an unknown. Or for a known solute it is possible to find out the extent of its ionization in the solvent because the depression of the freezing point is determined by the concentration of dissolved particles.

Crystal Structure and atomic radius. In crystalline solids, the atoms, ions or molecules are arranged in a definite patterns. This treatment will focus on two of the simplest repeating arrays, the body centered cube and the face centered cube. Many of the metals contain these crystal structures. These two arrays are illustrated in *Figures 18-4* and *18-5*.

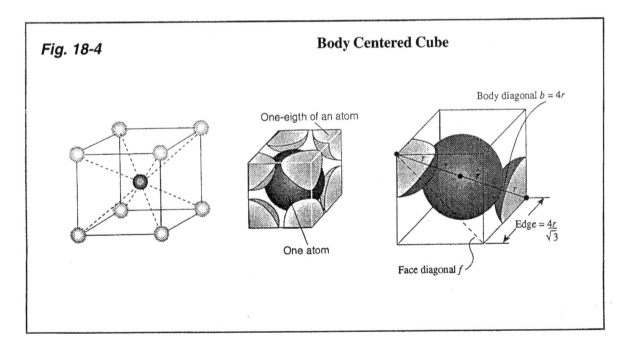

Fig. 18-4   **Body Centered Cube**

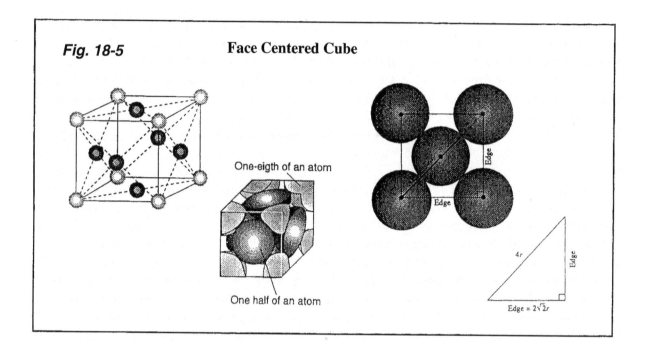

Fig. 18-5   **Face Centered Cube**

One-eigth of an atom

One half of an atom

Edge

Edge

4r

Edge

Edge = 2√2r

As can be seen from the drawings, the body centered cube has ⅛ of an atom at each corner and one in the center for a total of two atoms per unit cell. The cube diagonal is four times the radius of an atom and can be shown to be $3^{1/2}$ times the edge length of the cube.

The face centered cube has ⅛ of an atom in each corner and ½ in each of the six faces for a total of 4 atoms per unit cell. A face diagonal is four times the radius of an atom and is $2^{1/2}$ times the edge length of the cube.

If you performed ***Experiment 3***, you determined the density of a metal cylinder. If the crystal structure of an element is known and its density determined, it is possible with proper mathematical manipulation to calculate the atomic radius of the element. The calculation involves the use of the atomic mass, Avogadro's number, the number of atoms per unit cell and the density. For example, chromium with a density of 7.19 g/cm^3 crystallizes as a **body centered cubic** crystal. The volume V of its unit cell is:

$$V = \left(\frac{1\ cm^3}{7.19\ g}\right)\left(\frac{52.0\ g}{1\ mole}\right)\left(\frac{1\ mole}{6.022 \times 10^{23}\ atoms}\right)\left(\frac{2\ atoms}{unit\ cell}\right) = 2.40 \times 10^{-23}\ cm^3$$

The edge of the unit cell (a) is the cube root of the volume [$V^{1/3}$]

$$a = V^{1/3} = (2.40 \times 10^{-23}\ cm^3)^{1/3} = (24.0 \times 10^{-24}\ cm^3)^{1/3} = 2.89 \times 10^{-8}\ cm$$

$$atomic\ radius = r = a \times 3^{1/2}/4 = (2.89 \times 10^{-8}\ cm)(0.433) = 1.25 \times 10^{-8}\ cm$$

Procedure

A. Cooling Curves of lauric acid. For reasons stated in the *Notes to Students and Instructors*, lauric acid has been selected as the solvent for this experiment. There are many other possible solvents and some have significantly larger values of k_f. The larger the value of k_f, the larger the temperature depressions and this tends to decrease measurement errors. However, we have found supercooling to be a problem with many of the solvents that melt in the desired temperature range (40 - 50°C). With small modifications, the procedure below can be applied to other solvents but we hope you have more success than we did.

Weigh a clean and dry 18x150 mm test tube to 0.001 gram. Transfer about 4 g of lauric acid to the tube and reweigh the tube to the nearest 0.001 g. Clamp the test tube on a ring stand in a 400 mL beaker containing about 200 mL of water mounted over a wire gauze and a Bunsen burner. Insert a thermometer or temperature probe (preferably with a 0.1°C readout) into the test tube. Heat the water to about 50°C **(be sure if the thermometer has a range of 0 - 50°C that you do not exceed 50°C).** Raise the tube out of and away from the water bath and take temperature readings every 0.50 minutes for about the next 15 minutes. It is important to stir the sample with the thermometer between readings. The temperature will decrease at first, but will remain steady as the sample freezes. After the sample has solidified completely, the temperature will start dropping again. After it drops a few degrees below the plateau, the readings can be terminated.

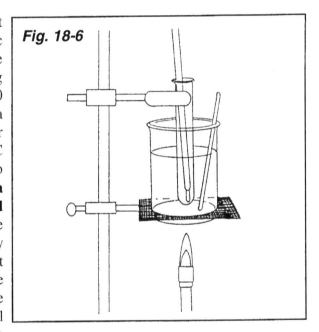

Fig. 18-6

Weigh out about 0.40 g of benzoic acid (weighed to the nearest 0.001 g) and add it to the test tube with the lauric acid. Insert the tube back into the water and repeat the procedure above. **Be sure to stir after melting.** Graphically determine the melting point depression caused by the benzoic acid and calculate the molecular mass of benzoic acid (k_f for lauric acid = 4.40°C kg/mol).

If the instructor desires, more than one trial of each of the above runs can be made or the molecular mass of an unknown can be determined.

B. Crystal structure and the atomic radius of a metal. Follow *Procedure C* in *Experiment 3* to determine the density of an unknown metallic element provided by your instructor. Use a method of your choice to determine the volume of the metal and weigh the metal to the nearest milligram. Compare your experimental density to values for aluminum, iron, copper and lead from the *Handbook of Chemistry and Physics* or *Appendix 1* and identify your metal. Using the information from the table below, your experimental density, the atomic mass and Avogadro's number, calculate the atomic radius of the metal. For example calculations, refer to the calculation on page 222 and to Problem 4 in the ***Prelaboratory Problems*** on page 226.

element	crystal structure
aluminum	face centered cubic
copper	face centered cubic
iron	body centered cubic
lead	face centered cubic

Name_____Date_____Lab Section_____

Prelaboratory Problems - *Experiment 18* - Cooling Curves and Crystal Structures   The solutions to the starred problems are in *Appendix 4*.

1. Melting point depression is termed a colligative property.

    a. What is the meaning of the word colligative?

    b. Which, if any of the following are colligative properties?

        density _____   boiling point elevation _____   color _____

2.* Naphthalene ($C_{10}H_8$) melts at 80.5°C. Addition of 0.38 grams of biphenyl ($C_{12}H_{10}$) to 5.00 g of naphthalene caused a melting point depression to 77.1°C.

    a. What is the freezing point depression constant of naphthalene?

    b. 0.150 g of anthracene ($C_{14}H_{10}$ - melting point = 216°C) is added to 3.00 g of naphthalene. At what temperature should the mixture start melting?

3. The freezing point depression constant of water is a rather small 1.86°C kg/mol.

    a. Addition of 0.100 g of an unknown compound to 2.50 g of water results in a decrease in the melting point of 2.3°C. What is the molecular mass of the unknown?

                                         molecular mass   _____

    b. Addition of 0.454 g of zinc chloride to 3.33 g of water lowers the melting point by 5.2°C. Calculate the expected melting point for this mixture and account for any difference.

                                    calculated melting point   _____

    c. What are some of the problems with the use of water as a solvent for determining the molecular mass of an unknown using the freezing point depression method?

4.* Nickel has a density of 8.90 g/cm^3 and crystallizes as a face centered cube. Calculate the atomic radius of nickel.

Name_____Date_____Lab Section_____

Results and Discussion - *Experiment 18* - Cooling Curves and Crystal Structures

A. Cooling Curves of Lauric Acid

   1.   Mass of test tube _____

   2.   Mass of test tube + lauric acid _____

   3.   Mass of lauric acid _____

Time (min.)	Temperature (°C)	Time (min.)	Temperature (°C)	Time (min.)	Temperature (°C)
0.00	_____	6.00	_____	12.00	_____
0.50	_____	6.50	_____	12.50	_____
1.00	_____	7.00	_____	13.00	_____
1.50	_____	7.50	_____	13.50	_____
2.00	_____	8.00	_____	14.00	_____
2.50	_____	8.50	_____	14.50	_____
3.00	_____	9.00	_____	15.00	_____
3.50	_____	9.50	_____	15.50	_____
4.00	_____	10.00	_____	16.00	_____
4.50	_____	10.50	_____	16.50	_____
5.00	_____	11.00	_____	17.00	_____
5.50	_____	11.50	_____	17.50	_____

   4.   Plot the temperature (y axis) versus time (x axis) and determine the melting point of lauric acid. _____

6.   Mass of benzoic acid   _____

Time (min.)	Temperature (°C)	Time (min.)	Temperature (°C)	Time (min.)	Temperature (°C)
0.00	_____	6.00	_____	12.00	_____
0.50	_____	6.50	_____	12.50	_____
1.00	_____	7.00	_____	13.00	_____
1.50	_____	7.50	_____	13.50	_____
2.00	_____	8.00	_____	14.00	_____
2.50	_____	8.50	_____	14.50	_____
3.00	_____	9.00	_____	15.00	_____
3.50	_____	9.50	_____	15.50	_____
4.00	_____	10.00	_____	16.00	_____
4.50	_____	10.50	_____	16.50	_____
5.00	_____	11.00	_____	17.00	_____
5.50	_____	11.50	_____	17.50	_____

7.   Plot the temperature (y axis) versus time and determine the melting point of lauric acid + benzoic acid.   _____

8.   Freezing point depression (Δt_f)   _____

9.   Molality of solution (according to the *International Critical Tables*, k_f for lauric acid is 4.40°C kg/mol)   _____

10.   Moles of solute in original sample   _____

11.   Molecular mass of benzoic acid from freezing point depression   _____

12.   Molecular mass of benzoic acid from formula ($C_7H_6O_2$)   _____

13.   Percent error   _____

14.   Suggest explanations for the percent error.

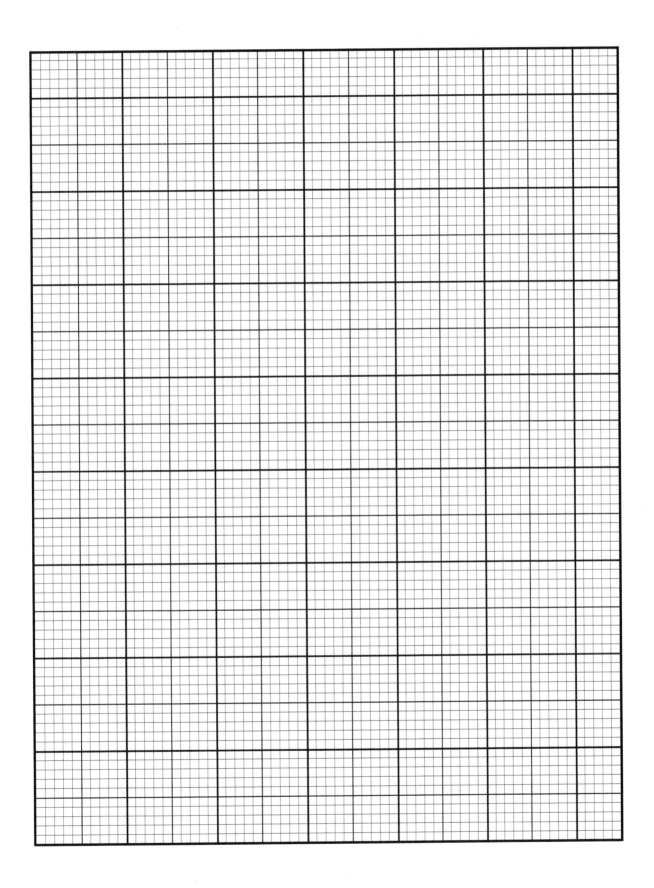

B. Crystal Structure and Atomic Radius of a Metal.

1. Density determination and identification of metal

   a. Identification number of metal cylinder   _____

   b. Mass of metal cylinder   _____

   c. Describe the method used to determine the volume of cylinder and give
       the data.

   d. Volume of metal cylinder   _____

   e. Density of metal cylinder   _____

   Handbook of Chemistry and Physics values for the density of:

   f. aluminum   _____

   g. copper   _____

   h. iron   _____

   i. lead   _____

   j. Identity of metal   _____

2. Atomic radius of metal

   a. Volume of unit cell (show calculations)   _____

   b. Edge length of cell   _____

   c. Atomic radius   _____

3.   Some of the *Learning Objectives* of this experiment are listed on the first page of this experiment. Did you achieve the *Learning Objectives*? Explain your answer.

Name_____Date_____Lab Section_____

Postlaboratory Problems - *Experiment 18* - Cooling Curves and Crystal Structures

1. How do you account for the trend of melting points in the series of acids to the right?

acid	formula	m.p. (°C)
octanoic (caprylic)	$C_8H_{16}O_2$	17.5
decanoic (capric)	$C_{10}H_{20}O_2$	31.5
dodecanoic (lauric)	$C_{12}H_{24}O_2$	44
tetradecanoic (myristic)	$C_{14}H_{28}O_2$	55
hexadecanoic (palmitic)	$C_{16}H_{32}O_2$	63
octadecanoic (stearic)	$C_{18}H_{36}O_2$	71
eicosanoic (arachidic)	$C_{20}H_{40}O_2$	77

2. List criteria that you think were used for selection of lauric acid as the solvent for today's experiment.

3. Lange's *Handbook of Chemistry* lists k_f values for acetic acid, benzene, camphor, strontium chloride and water as 3.9, 5.12, 37.7, 107 and 1.86 °C/m respectively. Why do you think each of the above solvents was eliminated from consideration for this experiment?

acetic acid

benzene

camphor

strontium chloride

water

4. Considering the other methods you have used that could be used to determine molecular mass such as titration and quantitative precipitation, when would the melting point depression method be used? Explain in detail.

5. Suggest any ways you can think of to improve any part(s) of this experiment.

15

ACIDS AND BASES: REACTIONS AND STANDARDIZATION

Learning Objectives

Upon completion of this experiment, students will have experienced:
1. Observation of common reactions of acids and bases.
2. The preparation and standardization of a sodium hydroxide solution.
3. The solving of a 4 unknown bottle acid and base system.

Text Topics

Acids and bases, indicators, titrations, standardizations (see page ix).

Notes to Students and Instructor

A solution of sodium hydroxide will be prepared and standardized by titration of the primary standard, potassium hydrogen phthalate. The standardized sodium hydroxide will be used as the titrant in *Experiments 22 - 25*. Time can be conserved if the instructor prepares the aqueous red cabbage solution.

Discussion

The word "acid" strikes fear in the minds of some people. While acids and bases need to be treated with care and respect, they are extremely important to us. To name a few examples of acids, HCl in our stomachs assists digestion, orange juice and vinegar are part of many meals and sulfuric acid, the most produced synthetic chemical, is used to catalyze a multitude of reactions. Bases such as sodium hydrogen carbonate in baking soda, sodium hydroxide in drain cleaners and ammonia in many household cleaners are also used for many applications. Like most chemicals, acids and bases are dangerous if abused. Solutions containing high concentrations of acids or bases will break down protein and therefore can cause severe burns if not washed off of the skin promptly after contact.

Why is it that compounds with hydrogen as the cation or hydroxide as the anion deserve to have the special names, acids and bases respectively? Sodium and chloride compounds do not get special names. One of the reasons is because hydrogen and hydroxide ions are good catalysts for many types of reactions including the decomposition of proteins such as skin.

This experiment is the first of four experiments that focus on the properties and reactions of acids and bases. Today, you will explore and review some reactions of acids and bases and acid-base indicators, prepare and standardize a sodium hydroxide solution and determine the contents of four unlabeled bottles of acids and bases.

Procedure

A. Reactions and indicators.

1. Measure the temperature of 2 mL of 3 M HCl in a test tube. Add 2 mL of 3 M NaOH to the tube, stir and record the maximum temperature attained.

2. Add 1 mL of 3 M HCl to 1 mL of 1 M sodium carbonate solution in a **large** test tube. Insert a lighted splint into the top portion of the test tube and report your observations.

3. Transfer 3 mL of 3 M NaOH to a test tube, add a small wad of aluminum foil and observe. After the reaction becomes vigorous, hold a lighted splint over the mouth of the test tube. *[Caution: Be sure the tube is not pointing at anyone during the course of this experiment.]*

4. Three solutions will be available.

> Solution A: 4 g soluble starch and 2 g of $Na_2S_2O_5$ (or 2.2 g $NaHSO_3$) in 1 liter of water. Prepare by dissolving 4 g of soluble starch in 1 liter of boiling water and adding 2 g of $Na_2S_2O_5$ (or 2.2 g $NaHSO_3$) after cooling.

> Solution B: 2 g KIO_3 and 1 mL of 3 M H_2SO_4 in 1 L of water

> Solution C: 2 g KIO_3 and 2 mL of 3 M H_2SO_4 in 1 L of water

> a.   Transfer 10 ml of solution A with a graduated cylinder to a flask. Quickly add 10 mL of solution B to the flask, **swirl** and determine the time elapsed before a change occurs.

> b.   Repeat a but use 10 mL of solution C in place of solution B.

5. Set up 12 test tubes and transfer 2 mL of 0.01 M HCl to the first four, 2 mL of a pH 7 buffer to the middle four and 2 mL of 0.01 M NaOH to the last four. Add 5 drops of phenolphthalein indicator to the first, fifth and ninth tubes, 5 drops of methyl orange indicator to the second, sixth and tenth tubes, 5 drops of bromothymol blue to the third, seventh and eleventh tubes and concentrated boiled aqueous red cabbage solution (cover some dark purple shredded red cabbage leaves with water in a small beaker and boil until the water is dark purple) to the fourth, eighth and twelfth tubes. Report your observations.

B. Standardization of sodium hydroxide solution. In future experiments, you will need standardized sodium hydroxide to determine the mass percent of acetic acid in vinegar, the formula mass of an unknown acid, the titration curves of HCl and acetic acid, the formula mass of a carbonate, the effectiveness of an antacid and the solubility of potassium hydrogen tartrate in water. As sodium hydroxide cannot be used as a primary standard, a titration must be performed to determine its concentration accurately. One of the most convenient primary standards for this purpose is **potassium hydrogen phthalate (KHP)**. KHP is a monoprotic organic acid with a formula mass of 204.22 g/mol. Note that the K and H stand for potassium and hydrogen respectively but the P stands for phthalate, not phosphorous.

1. Preparation of a 0.26 M NaOH solution. Do either option a or b at the discretion of the instructor. *Note that sodium hydroxide pellets (option a) are dangerously corrosive and should be handled with great care. The 6 M sodium hydroxide solution used in option b avoids the use of the pellets but is also a corrosive solution. If any sodium hydroxide solution is spilled on skin, it should be immediately washed off with a large quantity of water. The presence of sodium hydroxide (or other bases) on skin can usually be detected by its slippery feeling.*

    a. Weigh out about 10 g of NaOH pellets and transfer them to a 1 L bottle (preferably plastic as NaOH etches glass) [Note: 5 g of NaOH in a 500 mL bottle will suffice if only some of the *Experiments 22 - 25* are to be performed]. Add about 600 mL of deionized water and mix until the NaOH dissolves. Add another 350 mL of deionized water and mix again. Stopper, label and save this solution for the experiments today and next few weeks.

    b. Using a 50 mL graduated cylinder, transfer about 41 mL of the laboratory stock solution of 6 M NaOH to a 1 L bottle (preferably plastic as NaOH etches glass) [Note: 20 mL of NaOH in a 500 mL bottle will suffice if only some of the *Experiments 22 - 25* are to be performed]. Add about 900 mL of water and thoroughly mix the contents. Stopper, label and save this solution for the experiments today and next few weeks.

2.   Label three clean Erlenmeyer flasks 1, 2, and 3 and weigh into each of them 1 to 1.2 g of dry KHP to at least the nearest 0.001 g. Add about 50 mL of water to each flask and swirl to dissolve the KHP. Rinse and fill a 50 mL buret with the NaOH solution. Add 2 or 3 drops of phenolphthalein to flask #1 and titrate (see *Figures 21-1* and *21-2*) until the first tinge of pink appears. As you approach the end point, the pink will persist for longer periods of time before fading to colorless. At this point add the NaOH in half drop quantities by rapidly turning the closed stopcock 180° (see *Figure 21-1*). Repeat the titrations on flasks 2 and 3.

C. Four acid and base unknowns. For this challenge, you will have available a set of 4 bottles labeled only A, B, C and D. The bottles will contain 0.1 M HCl, 0.4 M HCl, 0.1 M NaOH and 0.4 M NaOH. Each of the acid unknowns also contains phenolphthalein (colorless in acid and pink in base). No other reagents or test papers may be used but the solutions can be mixed with each other. Before you attack this problem, think about the various possibilities when two solutions are mixed including the order of mixing and develop a scheme that will enable you to identify the contents of the 4 bottles.

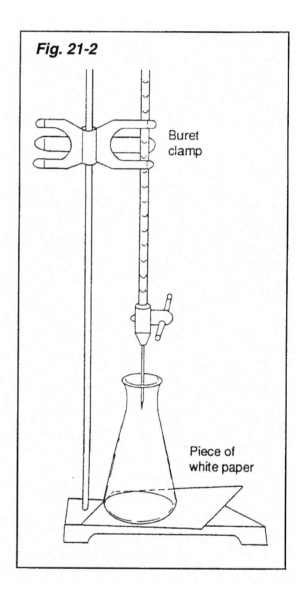

Fig. 21-2

Buret clamp

Piece of white paper

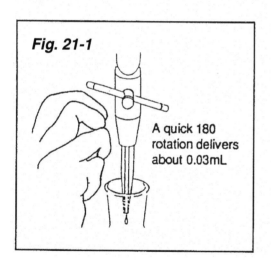

Fig. 21-1

A quick 180 rotation delivers about 0.03mL

Name_____Date_____Lab Section_____

Prelaboratory Problems - *Experiment 21* - **Acids and Bases: Reactions and Standardization**   The solutions to the starred problems are in *Appendix 4*.

1. a.   Option 1-a of the instructions suggests the dissolving of about 10 g of NaOH in 0.95 L of water to prepare the solution to be standardized. Calculate the approximate concentration of this solution.

_____

   b.   Option 1-b of the instructions suggests that about 41 mL of 6 M NaOH be diluted to about 0.95 L of water to prepare the solution to be standardized. Calculate the approximate concentration of this solution.

_____

   c.*   1 to 1.2 gram samples of KHP (204.22 g/mol, potassium hydrogen phthalate, not potassium hydrogen phosphorous) will be used to standardize the NaOH solution. Approximately what volume of the NaOH solution will be required to titrate the KHP?

_____

   d.   Why would it have been very inaccurate to have just weighed out 10.000 g of NaOH, diluted it to 1.000 L and calculated the molarity without standardizing it (in other words, can NaOH be used as a primary standard?)?

2.* A 0.4904 g sample of KHP requires 23.82 mL of NaOH to reach the end point. What is the concentration of NaOH?

3. A 0.3535 g sample of KHP requires 19.27 mL of NaOH to reach the end point. What is the concentration of NaOH?

4. What properties should the indicator have for titration of KHP with NaOH?

5. Give a detailed scheme (preferably illustrated with a matrix - see **Experiment 9**) with predicted observations for the analysis of the acids and bases in *Part C*. Be sure to consider order of mixing. Also enter your plan on page 263 for *Problem C*. What is the minimum number of mixtures needed to solve the system?

Name_____Date_____Lab Section_____

Results and Discussion - *Experiment 21* - Acids and Bases: Reactions and Standardization

A. Reactions and indicators.

For numbers 1 - 3 below, report your observations and write balanced equations for each reaction.

1. hydrochloric acid + sodium hydroxide

temperature of HCl   _____

temperature after mixing   _____

2. hydrochloric acid + sodium carbonate solution

3. sodium hydroxide solution + aluminum

    evolved gas + oxygen

4. Observations for A + B   time elapsed   _____

    Observations for A + C   time elapsed   _____

    Does it appear that hydrogen ion catalyzes the process that is responsible for the observed change? Explain your answer.

5. Color chart of indicators in 0.01 M HCl, pH 7 buffer, 0.01 M NaOH

	0.01 M HCl	pH 7 buffer	0.01 M NaOH
phenolphthalein	_____	_____	_____
methyl orange	_____	_____	_____
bromothymol blue	_____	_____	_____
red cabbage extract	_____	_____	_____

B. Standardization of sodium hydroxide solution.

	flask 1	flask 2	flask 3
1. Mass of flask + KHP[1]	_____	_____	_____
2. Mass of flask	_____	_____	_____
3. Mass of KHP	_____	_____	_____
4. Moles of KHP (204.22 g/mole)	_____	_____	_____
5. Final buret reading	_____	_____	_____
6. Initial buret reading	_____	_____	_____
7. Volume of NaOH soln.	_____	_____	_____
8. Molarity of NaOH soln.	_____	_____	_____
9. Average molarity of NaOH solution (Record also in next 4 experiments)			_____
10. Deviation from average	_____	_____	_____
11. Average deviation of molarity (see *Expt. 4*)			_____

_____

[1]KHP stands for potassium hydrogen phthalate, 204.22 g/mol, not potassium hydrogen phosphous.

C. Four acid and base unknowns.

1.   Give your scheme (see *Prelaboratory Exercise 5*) for identifying the four solutions and the observations. Include prediction and observation matrices. Be sure to consider the order of mixing.

2.   Give the compound and the concentration for each bottle.

A = _____   B = _____   C = _____   D = _____

3.   Suggest any ways you can think of to improve any part(s) of this experiment.

4.   Some of the *Learning Objectives* of this experiment are listed on the first page of this experiment. Did you achieve the *Learning Objectives*? Explain your answer.

16

ACIDS AND BASES: ANALYSIS

vinegar

Learning Objectives

Upon completion of this experiment, students will have experienced:
1. The determination of the percent by mass of acetic acid in vinegar.
2. The determination of the molecular mass of an unknown acid.

Text Topics

Acids and bases, indicators, titrations, (for correlation to some texts, see page ix).

Notes to Students and Instructor

The solution of sodium hydroxide prepared last week will be used to determine the percent by mass of acetic acid in vinegar and to determine the molecular mass of an unknown acid.

Discussion

Have you ever tasted wine that has gone sour? The taste is due to the presence of acetic acid which results from the oxidation of the ethanol in the wine. In fact vinegar is produced by fermentation of sugar to ethanol followed by bacteria catalyzed oxidation of the ethanol to acetic acid. One question that a chemist might be confronted with is how much acetic acid is present in the vinegar. This is just one of the questions commonly encountered by chemists working in analytical laboratories. Another challenge might be the identification of an acid in a sample. The determination of its molecular mass can go a long way toward facilitating this identification. The amount of acetic acid in vinegar and the molecular mass of an unknown acid can be determined by titration with a standardized base. These are the topics for today's experiment.

Procedure

A.   Titration of vinegar.   In ***Experiment 21***, you prepared and standardized an approximately 0.2 M NaOH solution. Because vinegar is close to 1 M acetic acid, it is advisable either to quantitatively dilute the vinegar or titrate only 5.00 mL quantities to avoid using more than 1 buret full of sodium hydroxide. The use of 5.00 mL delivered with a volumetric pipet is suggested.

Obtain a vinegar unknown from your instructor. Weigh a 125 or 250 mL Erlenmeyer flask and pipet 5.00 mL of vinegar into the flask. Reweigh the flask and calculate the density of the vinegar solution. Add about 50 mL of water and 3 drops of phenolphthalein and titrate with the standardized sodium hydroxide until the first tinge of pink persists. Repeat the titration two more times and calculate the molarity and mass percent of acetic acid in vinegar.

B. Molecular mass of an unknown acid.   Obtain an unknown acid from your instructor. Weigh approximately 0.5 g samples to at least the nearest 0.001 g into three Erlenmeyer flasks. Dissolve each of the samples in about 50 mL of water, add 3 drops of phenolphthalein indicator and titrate with standardized sodium hydroxide. Repeat for the second and third samples. Calculate the molecular mass for each trial and the average molecular mass.

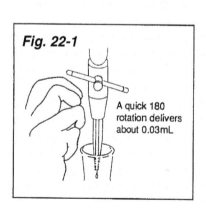

Fig. 22-1

A quick 180 rotation delivers about 0.03mL

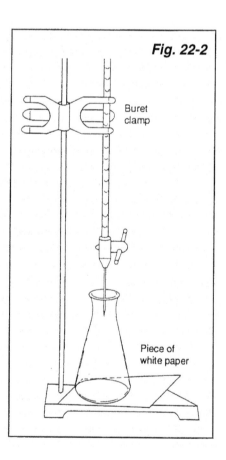

Fig. 22-2

Buret clamp

Piece of white paper

Name_____Date_____Lab Section_____

Prelaboratory Problems - *Experiment 22* - Acids and Bases: Analysis
The solutions to the starred problems are in *Appendix 4*.

1.* The titration of 25.00 mL of a sulfuric acid solution of unknown concentration requires 31.22 mL of a 0.1234 M NaOH solution. What is the concentration of the sulfuric acid solution?

2.* 10.00 mL of vinegar (mass = 10.05 g) requires 16.28 mL of 0.5120 M NaOH to reach the end point. Calculate the molarity and mass percent of the acetic acid in the vinegar.

3.* A 0.1936 g sample of an unknown monoprotic acid requires 15.56 mL of 0.1020 M NaOH solution to reach the end point. What is the molecular mass of the acid?

4. The titration of 10.00 mL of a diprotic acid solution of unknown concentration requires 21.37 mL of a 0.1432 M NaOH solution. What is the concentration of the diprotic acid solution?

5. 10.00 mL of vinegar (mass = 10.05 g) requires 14.77 mL of 0.4926 M NaOH to reach the end point. Calculate the molarity and mass percent of the acetic acid in the vinegar.

6. A 0.2602 g sample of an unknown monoprotic acid requires 12.23 mL of 0.1298 M NaOH solution to reach the end point. What is the molecular mass of the acid?

Name_____Date_____Lab Section_____

Results and Discussion - *Experiment 22* - Acids and Bases: Analysis

A. Analysis of vinegar

1.   Unknown vinegar number   _____

2.   Mass of flask   _____

3.   Mass of flask + 5.00 mL of vinegar   _____

4.   Mass of 5.00 mL of vinegar   _____

5.   Density of vinegar   _____

6.   Molarity of sodium hydroxide solution   _____

Titrations	flask 1	flask 2	flask 3
7. Final buret reading	_____	_____	_____
8. Initial buret reading	_____	_____	_____
9. Volume of NaOH soln.	_____	_____	_____
10. Moles of NaOH	_____	_____	_____
11. Moles of acetic acid	_____	_____	_____
12. Molarity of acetic acid	_____	_____	_____

13.   Average molarity of acetic
      acid in vinegar   _____

14.   Deviation of each
      molarity from average   _____   _____   _____

15.   Average deviation of molarity (see *Expt. 4*)   _____

16.   Mass percent of acetic acid in vinegar   _____
      (show calculations below)

B. Molecular mass of an unknown acid.

1. Unknown number   _____

2. Molarity of sodium hydroxide solution   _____

Titrations	flask 1	flask 2	flask 3

3. Mass of flask + unk.   _____   _____   _____

4. Mass of flask   _____   _____   _____

5. Mass of unknown   _____   _____   _____

6. Final buret reading   _____   _____   _____

8. Initial buret reading   _____   _____   _____

9. Volume of NaOH soln.   _____   _____   _____

10. Moles of unknown acid   _____   _____   _____
    (assume monoprotic)

11. Molecular mass of acid   _____   _____   _____

12. Average molecular mass
    of acid   _____

13. Deviation of each
    mol. mass from average   _____   _____   _____

14. Average deviation of molecular mass   _____

15. Suggest experimental modifications you could make if the acid to be titrated has low
    solubility in water.

16. Some of the *Learning Objectives* of this experiment are listed on the first page of this
    experiment. Did you achieve the *Learning Objectives*? Explain your answer.

Determining Hydrogen Peroxide Content by Gas Stoichiometry

Prepared by Patricia A. Metz, United States Naval Academy

PURPOSE OF THE EXPERIMENT

Measure the volume of oxygen produced by catalytic decomposition of hydrogen peroxide in an aqueous solution. Use gas stoichiometry to calculate the molarity and mass percent of hydrogen peroxide in the solution.

BACKGROUND REQUIRED

You should know how to collect a gas by water displacement. You should understand the concepts of the ideal gas equation, gas reaction stoichiometry, partial pressure of a gas, and decomposition reactions. You should be able to calculate molarity and mass percent.

SCENARIO

Several weeks ago, a nightshift plant worker at Nature's Best Vinegar Company overdiluted a batch of acetic acid and nearly ruined 20,000 gallons of vinegar. The reason for this mistake was a careless mathematical error. Realizing his chances for advancement with Nature's Best Vinegar Company were not good, the worker sought employment at the Global Hydrogen Peroxide plant. Global Hydrogen Peroxide makes two products: swimming pool shocker (aqueous hydrogen peroxide, 27–33% by mass) and household hydrogen peroxide (2.5–3.5% by mass).

Hydrogen peroxide is made by oxidation of an anthraquinol to an anthraquinone.

| 2-ethylanthraquinol | oxygen | 2-ethylanthraquinone | hydrogen peroxide |

$$\text{2-ethylanthraquinol} + O_2 \longrightarrow \text{2-ethylanthraquinone} + H_2O_2 \qquad \text{(Eq. 1)}$$

The hydrogen peroxide is extracted into water and diluted to the desired concentration.

The plant worker was hired and assigned, as all new employees are, to the nightshift. While making a batch of pool shocker last night, he thinks he may have made another calculation error and once again overdiluted a product.

Your job today is to determine the concentration of hydrogen peroxide in a sample taken from the batch. To do this, you will first catalytically decompose the hydrogen peroxide and collect the oxygen gas produced. Using the ideal gas equation, you will calculate the moles of oxygen produced from the sample. The reaction stoichiometry will help you calculate the moles of hydrogen peroxide reacted. You are to report the concentration of the hydrogen peroxide in molarity and mass percent. You will share your results with your classmates and calculate the class averages. Your final task in this investigation will be to write a calculation protocol for diluting any hydrogen peroxide solution to a specific concentration.

BACKGROUND INFORMATION

Hydrogen peroxide is an excellent oxidizing agent. In World War II, the military mixed hydrogen peroxide with rocket fuel and used it in torpedoes. Textile and paper manufacturers use it as a bleaching agent. Some municipal water companies use it to treat wastewater and drinking water. Consumers use a 3% solution of hydrogen peroxide as mild hair bleach or antiseptic and a 30% solution to treat swimming pool water overrun with microorganisms.

Even though hydrogen peroxide is a fairly stable compound, it will decompose slowly to form oxygen gas and water. Using a catalyst such as ordinary baker's yeast, beef liver, or potato pulp can accelerate this decomposition reaction. Science teachers often use this reaction to generate oxygen gas safely in their classrooms.

In this experiment, you will determine the molarity and mass percent of a hydrogen peroxide solution. Potassium iodide is the catalyst you will use to decompose your measured amount of hydrogen peroxide. You will collect the oxygen gas produced from the decomposition reaction by water displacement. Temperature, pressure, and oxygen gas volume measurements will be used to calculate the moles of oxygen gas. The moles of oxygen gas are stoichiometrically related to the moles of hydrogen peroxide reacted.

Name _____   Section _____   Date _____

Pre-Laboratory Assignment

(Use the spaces provided for the answers and additional paper if necessary.)

1. While measuring the hydrogen peroxide solution you will use in your experiment, suppose that you accidentally splashed some in your mouth. Explain how you would handle the situation.

2. **(a)** Write the ideal gas equation.

   (b) What does each variable represent?

3. Write a balanced chemical equation for the catalytic decomposition reaction of hydrogen peroxide. Indicate the physical state of each reactant and product, using the abbreviations: (aq) for aqueous solution, (s) for solid, (*l*) for liquid, and (g) for gas.

4. **(a)** In this experiment you will collect the oxygen gas produced by water displacement. Find information in your textbook, a laboratory manual, or a Web site about the technique of water displacement. Cite the sources of this information by listing the author or editor, book title, publisher, city of publication, publication date, and page number, for references in print, or the URL, for those on the Web.

   (b) Sketch the apparatus you will use for decomposing the hydrogen peroxide and collecting the oxygen gas produced by water displacement. Keep in mind that you must quantitatively measure the volume of gas you collect.

(c) The adjacent figure shows a gas collected over water in a test tube. Is the pressure of the gas above the water in the test tube greater than or less than atmospheric pressure? Briefly explain.

(d) What should you do to make the pressure of the gas equal to atmospheric pressure?

(e) Find a Web site that provides atmospheric (barometric) pressure for your area. List the date, time, geographical area, atmospheric pressure, and URL for the Web site.

(f) When a gas is collected by water displacement, water vapor is also present in the collection container. Dalton's law of partial pressures tells us the oxygen gas pressure plus the water vapor pressure equals the atmospheric pressure. Find a table of water vapor pressures at various temperatures. What is the water vapor pressure at 21.4 °C? Cite your reference.

5. Last week, a quality control technician for Global Hydrogen Peroxide determined the concentration of a batch of household hydrogen peroxide. She followed the instructions in the Laboratory Investigations section of this experiment and obtained this data:

volume of hydrogen peroxide, mL	8.72
barometric pressure, in. Hg	30.09
temperature of water, °C	21.4
volume of oxygen gas collected, mL	99.4

(a) What is the pressure, in atmospheres, of oxygen gas collected?

(b) Calculate the moles of oxygen gas collected.

(c) Calculate the moles of hydrogen peroxide reacted.

(d) Calculate the molarity of hydrogen peroxide solution.

(e) Calculate the mass percent of hydrogen peroxide solution.

6. The Laboratory Investigations section of this experiment describes what you will do in the laboratory in a general way, but it does not contain a detailed procedure. Your laboratory instructor may provide one or ask you to outline the steps you will follow, using the Laboratory Investigations Outline page of this module. You should write the outline in such a way that another student could use it to perform the experiment, without having to ask you any questions.

7. Because there is no data table provided for this experiment, your laboratory instructor may provide one. On the other hand, your laboratory instructor may ask you to:

    (a) determine which data you are going to collect, and

    (b) create a table to organize these data.

    If this is the case, organize and record your data on the Laboratory Investigations Data page for this module. Because not all of the measurements and observations you need to record may be obvious at first, leave plenty of space between the lines of your data table for data you may not have considered recording when you created the table.

Laboratory Investigations

Reagents

hydrogen peroxide sample   potassium iodide, solid

Special Equipment

100-mL graduated cylinder
90 cm plastic tubing
one-hole stopper to fit large test tube or small flask

Wear departmentally approved safety goggles at all times while in the chemistry laboratory.
   Always use caution in the laboratory. Many chemicals are potentially harmful. Immediately tell your laboratory instructor if you spill any reagents.

NOTE: Record all volume and temperature measurements using the number of significant figures specified by your laboratory instructor.
   Record all data and observations on your Laboratory Investigations Data sheet.
   Dispose of your reaction mixtures according to your laboratory instructor's directions.

Hydrogen peroxide is an irritant and oxidant. Potassium iodide is an irritant and moisture–sensitive.

1. Obtain 50 mL of hydrogen peroxide solution in a clean, *dry* beaker.
2. Obtain 3 cm^3 of potassium iodide in a clean, *dry* container.
3. Assemble your apparatus for decomposing hydrogen peroxide and collecting the oxygen gas produced by water displacement.
4. Use 7–9 mL of hydrogen peroxide solution (record the exact volume) and 0.5 cm^3 of potassium iodide for each decomposition reaction.
   Do 3–5 determinations, as specified by your laboratory instructor.
   Have your laboratory instructor check your data. If they are acceptable, your instructor will initial your Data Table.
5. Record the atmospheric pressure. Your laboratory instructor will tell you whether to get this measurement from a Web site or a barometer in the laboratory.

Suggestions

(a) Clamp the gas collection container to a ring stand for greater stability.
(b) Keep the reaction container in an upright position at all times by either holding it or clamping it to the ring stand.
(c) Record exact volumes of hydrogen peroxide used and oxygen gas produced.
(d) Use the water temperature for the temperature of gas collected.

6. *Cleanup and disposal.* Dispose of your reaction mixtures as directed by your laboratory instructor. Wash all equipment with soap or detergent. Rinse with tap water, then distilled water, and dry.

CAUTION

Wash your hands thoroughly with soap or detergent before leaving the laboratory.

Name   _Section_   _Date_

Laboratory Investigations Outline

Laboratory Investigations Data

Name   Section   Date

Post-Laboratory Questions

(Use the spaces provided for the answers and additional paper if necessary.)

   1. Calculate partial pressure, in atmospheres, of oxygen gas collected.

   2. Calculate the following for each of your determinations.

   (a) moles of oxygen gas produced

   (b) moles of hydrogen peroxide reacted

   (c) molarity of hydrogen peroxide solution

   (d) mass percent of hydrogen peroxide solution

   3. Construct a table of results. Show the moles of oxygen gas produced, moles of hydrogen peroxide reacted, molarity of hydrogen peroxide solution, and mass percent of hydrogen peroxide solution for each determination you did.

   4. (a) Calculate your average molarity of hydrogen peroxide.

   (b) Calculate your average mass percent of hydrogen peroxide.

   (c) Calculate the class average molarity of hydrogen peroxide.

   (d) Calculate the class average mass percent of hydrogen peroxide.

5. Is the hydrogen peroxide too dilute to be sold by Global Hydrogen Peroxide as swimming pool shocker? Can they sell it as household hydrogen peroxide? Briefly explain.

6. When the Global Hydrogen Peroxide quality control technician first learned to do concentration determinations, she made the following procedural errors. In each case, state whether the calculated molarity would have been higher than, lower than, or the same as the actual molarity. Briefly explain each answer.

   (a) She used a beaker with water in it to obtain her hydrogen peroxide solution.

   (b) She did not take water vapor pressure into consideration when doing the calculations.

   (c) She used double the amount of potassium iodide than recommended.

   (d) She did not stopper her reaction container quickly after adding the potassium iodide to the hydrogen peroxide solution.

7. On a separate sheet of paper write an easy to follow calculation protocol for shift workers diluting any volume, and any concentration, of hydrogen peroxide to a specific mass percent. Show a general equation into which the initial volume, initial concentration, and desired mass percent can be inserted. Then show a specific example where the initial volume is 1,500 gal, the initial concentration is 42% by mass, and the desired mass percent is 30%.

8. (a) Calculate the theoretical volume of oxygen gas that could be produced from the decomposition of 8.75 mL of 30% hydrogen peroxide at STP.

   (b) If the plant worker had correctly made 30% hydrogen peroxide, how would this affect your laboratory investigation?

   (c) What changes, if any, would you make to your procedure?

Determining the Thickness of Zinc on Galvanized Washers

Prepared by Patricia A. Metz, United States Naval Academy

PURPOSE OF THE EXPERIMENT

Determine how many millimeters of zinc and layers of zinc atoms are present on a galvanized steel washer.

BACKGROUND REQUIRED

You should know how to weigh solid samples. You should understand the relationship among moles, number of atoms, and mass of an element. You should be able to calculate the circumference and area of a circle.

SCENARIO

Consolidated Metal is submitting a bid for a government contract to make galvanized steel washers. If awarded the contract, Consolidated is guaranteed the sale of 250,000 washers a year for three years. Iron and steel objects exposed to moisture and air will rust. Coating the object with zinc in a treatment known as galvanizing deters rusting. The government contract requires a zinc coating of 0.045–0.055 mm with a 98% tolerance. This means 98 washers out of 100 have the proper thickness. All bids must include a quality control report verifying that the bidding company's galvanizing process meets these specifications. Consolidated Metal would like your assistance with their quality control report. A sample of galvanized steel washers from last Monday's production run has been sent to your laboratory. Your task is to measure the dimensions and mass of the washers, chemically remove the zinc coating, and then measure the mass again. From these data and the density and atomic radii of zinc you will calculate the thickness (in both millimeters and number of atoms) of the zinc coating on the washers. The results from all the students in your laboratory class will be pooled and you will write a report to the president of Consolidated Metal supporting or rejecting their bid for the government contract.

BACKGROUND INFORMATION

Most metals corrode when exposed to the atmosphere. Some corrode more quickly due to their intrinsic nature. The corrosion or rusting of structural materials like iron and steel (an iron alloy) is both costly and dangerous. To slow the rusting process products such as nails, sheet metal, pipes, and washers are galvanized or coated with zinc, a more reactive metal. If the zinc coating is scratched and the iron exposed, the iron is still protected by sacrificial corrosion. In other words the zinc reacts while the iron is spared.

The zinc coating is applied to the iron or steel object by electroplating. In this process the item to be galvanized is suspended from an electrode in a container of molten zinc chloride. An electric current is passed through the system, causing zinc atoms to bond to the surface of the object. The longer the electricity is applied, the thicker the zinc coating.

In this experiment we are interested in removing, not depositing, the zinc coating on a washer. Aside from reacting with water and oxygen in the atmosphere, metals react readily with acid. When a galvanized washer is placed in hydrochloric acid, the zinc coating is removed and converted into aqueous zinc chloride. The iron core remains intact because it is less reactive than the zinc. By weighing the washer before and after the reaction you can determine the mass of the zinc coating.

In the laboratory you will measure the dimensions of several washers and calculate the total surface area of the zinc coating. Then you will chemically remove the coating and determine the mass of zinc on the washer. These data, together with the density of zinc, will allow you to calculate the thickness of the coating in millimeters. You can then use the atomic radius of a zinc atom to determine how many atoms thick the coating is. After collecting the results of all the students in your class you will calculate the average thickness and percent tolerance.

Name   *Section*   *Date*

Pre-Laboratory Assignments

(Use the spaces provided for the answers and additional paper if necessary.)

1. The safety caution in the Laboratory Investigations section states no flames are allowed in the laboratory during this experiment. Which reactants and/or products warrant this precaution? Briefly explain.

2. In addition to your laboratory measurements, you will need to know the density of zinc and atomic radius of a zinc atom. Find this information about zinc in your textbook, a chemistry handbook, or a Web site. Cite the sources of this information by listing the author or editor, book title, publisher, city of publication, publication date, and page number, for references in print, or the URL, for those on the Web.

3. A technician at Consolidated Metal determined the thickness of zinc on a galvanized washer following the instructions in the Laboratory Investigations section of this experiment. He collected these data.

outer diameter of washer, mm	26.4
inner diameter of washer, mm	10.8
height of washer, mm	2.2
mass of washer before reaction, g	8.473
mass of washer after reaction, g	7.957

(a) Calculate the volume, in cubic millimeters (mm^3), of the zinc coating.

(b) Calculate the total surface area, in square millimeters (mm^2), of the washer.

(c) Calculate the thickness, in millimeters, of the zinc coating.

(d) Calculate the thickness, in number of atoms, of the zinc coating. Assume that layers of zinc atoms stack directly one on top of the other.

4. Write a balanced chemical equation for the reaction of zinc metal with hydrochloric acid to form hydrogen gas and zinc chloride in solution. Indicate the physical state of each reactant and product, using the abbreviations: (aq) for aqueous solution, (s) for solid, (ℓ) for liquid, and (g) for gas.

5. The Laboratory Investigations section of this experiment describes what you will do in the laboratory in a general way, but it does not contain a detailed procedure. Your laboratory instructor may provide one or ask you to outline the steps you will follow, using the Laboratory Investigations Outline page of this module. You should write the outline in such a way that another student could use it to perform the experiment, without having to ask you any questions.

6. Because there is no data table provided for this experiment, your laboratory instructor may provide one. On the other hand, your laboratory instructor may ask you to:

   (a) determine which data you are going to collect, and
   (b) create a table to organize these data.

   If this is the case, organize and record your data on the Laboratory Investigations Data page for this module. Because not all of the measurements and observations you need to record may be obvious at first, leave plenty of space between the lines of your data table, for data you may not have considered recording when you created the table.

LABORATORY INVESTIGATIONS

Reagents

galvanized washers   3M hydrochloric acid

Special Equipment

metric ruler marked in millimeters

CAUTION

Wear departmentally approved safety goggles at all times while in the chemistry laboratory.

Always use caution in the laboratory. Many chemicals are potentially harmful. Immediately tell your laboratory instructor if you spill any reagents.

No open flames are permitted during this experiment.

NOTE: Record all data and observations on your Laboratory Investigations Data sheet.

Dispose of your reaction mixtures according to your laboratory instructor's directions.

Record all measurements using the number of significant figures specified by your laboratory instructor.

1. Obtain three to five galvanized washers as directed by your laboratory instructor. Measure the dimensions and mass of each washer; record them on your Laboratory Investigations Data page. Record a physical description of each washer.

CAUTION

Hydrochloric acid is toxic and corrosive.
Hydrogen gas, formed in Step 2, is flammable.
Avoid breathing the vapor produced in Step 2.

2. Obtain 10 mL of 3M hydrochloric acid in a small beaker. Place one washer in the acid and let it react until the vigorous effervescence stops. Remove the washer, rinse with distilled or deionized water, and dry. Record the mass of the washer on your Laboratory Investigations Data page.

3. Dispose of the reaction mixture as indicated by your laboratory instructor.

4. Repeat Steps 2 and 3 with your other washers.

5. *Cleanup and disposal.* Place washers in the "Recovered Washer" container. Wash all equipment with soap or detergent, rinse with tap water and then with distilled water, and dry.

CAUTION

Wash your hands thoroughly with soap or detergent before leaving the laboratory.

Name _____ Section _____ Date _____

Laboratory Investigations Outline

Laboratory Investigations Data

Name _____ Section _____ Date _____

Post-Laboratory Questions

(Use the spaces provided for the answers and additional paper if necessary.)

1. For each washer, calculate these values and summarize your results in a table.

    (a) volume of the zinc coating in cubic millimeters
    (b) total surface area in square millimeters
    (c) thickness of the zinc coating in millimeters
    (d) thickness of the zinc coating in number of atoms

2. Compile class data for the thickness of the zinc coating in both millimeters and number of atoms. Calculate the average for each unit.

3. Based on the class average thickness of the zinc coating, was last Monday's batch of galvanized washers produced by Consolidated Metal within the required government specifications for both thickness and tolerance?

4. A new technician at Consolidated Metal made several mistakes when learning the procedure for determining the thickness of zinc on galvanized washers. Would these mistakes cause the calculated thickness of the zinc coating to be higher, lower, or the same as the actual thickness? Briefly explain.

(a) He used 20 mL of $3M$ hydrochloric acid instead of 10 mL.

(b) He removed the washer from the hydrochloric acid before the reaction stopped effervescing.

(c) He left the washer in the hydrochloric acid while he went to lunch.

(d) He used $0.3M$ hydrochloric acid instead of $3M$.

5. On a separate sheet of paper, write a report to the president of Consolidated Metal summarizing your laboratory class results and either supporting or rejecting their bid for the government contract.

6. The electroplating process used by Consolidated Metal is designed to galvanize 200 washers per batch with each washer having an average 0.35 g zinc coating. If Consolidated uses an electrical current of 175 amperes(A), how many hours will it take to produce the 250,000 washers required by the government contract? Useful information:

$$1 \text{ A current} = 1 \text{ coulomb(C) charge/s}$$
$$1 \text{ mol electrons}/96{,}485 \text{ C}$$
$$2 \text{ mol electrons}/1 \text{ mol Zn}$$

Applying the Concept of a Limiting Reactant to the Synthesis of Aspirin

Prepared by Patricia A. Metz, United States Naval Academy

PURPOSE OF THE EXPERIMENT

Determine the most cost-effective limiting reactant, for the synthesis of aspirin. Synthesize aspirin and determine its degree of purity.

BACKGROUND REQUIRED

You should know how to do a vacuum filtration and a titration. You should understand the concepts of reaction stoichiometry and limiting reactants. You should be able to calculate theoretical and percent yields, and percent purity.

SCENARIO

Students in a college marketing course are working with the development division of Atkinson Health Products. Atkinson is a local company with a diverse line of over-the-counter health and wellness products. Their top products include dandruff shampoo, therapeutic bath salts, athlete's foot powder, acne cleanser, and sunscreen lotion. All of these products are applied to the body; none are ingested. The company's president feels the time has come for expansion into the oral medication market. The first product under consideration is aspirin. To start the process, the marketing students have been asked to do a cost analysis for the synthesis of aspirin. Someone in the course remembered from his high school chemistry class that all reactions do not yield 100% product and that the product is often not pure. Students in the marketing course need to know this information for aspirin synthesis. In this experiment you will make a small batch of aspirin, then you will determine its percent yield and its percent purity.

BACKGROUND INFORMATION

The ancient Romans were the first to discover the fever- and pain-reducing benefits of an aspirin-like substance called salicin, which is found in the bark and leaves of willow trees. In 1897, Felix Hoffman, a German chemist employed by Friedrich Baeyer and Company, synthesized acetylsalicylic acid, now commonly known as aspirin. Soon aspirin was marketed as an analgesic (pain reliever), an antipyretic (fever reducer), and an anti-inflammatory medicine.

Although aspirin's ability to relieve pain, fever, and inflammation was known since the turn of the century, no one knew how aspirin did this. Pharmacologist John Vane discovered how aspirin functions in the body and was awarded the 1982 Nobel Prize for Medicine.

Aspirin is made by treating salicylic acid with acetic anhydride in the presence of an acid catalyst such as sulfuric or phosphoric acid. A by-product of the reaction is acetic acid. Pharmaceutical companies, like all chemical companies, keep their production cost low by making the most expensive reactant the limiting reactant. To ensure that all the limiting reactant is consumed, they use a large excess of the cheaper reactant(s) to drive the reaction to completion. Completion does not mean necessarily 100% yield. Under optimal conditions the highest yield you can expect for your synthesis of aspirin is 60%.

In this experiment, first you will determine the amount of reactants needed to make the quantity of aspirin found in 10 aspirin tablets. Next you will synthesize the aspirin and calculate your percent yield. Then, you will determine the percent purity of your aspirin by titrating with a standard sodium hydroxide solution. Finally, you will write a memorandum to the students in the marketing course summarizing your aspirin synthesis findings.

Name _____   Section _____   Date _____

Pre-Laboratory Assignments

(Use the spaces provided for the answers and additional paper if necessary.)

1. Acetic anhydride is characterized as a corrosive substance and a lachrymator.

   (a) What do these terms mean?

   (b) What precautions should you take when handling acetic anhydride?

2. In this experiment you will apply the concept of a limiting reactant to the synthesis of aspirin. Find information in your textbook, a science encyclopedia, or a Web site about limiting reactants.

   (a) Cite the sources of this information by listing the author or editor, book title, publisher, city of publication, publication date, and page number, for references in print, or the URL, for those on the Web.

   (b) What nonchemical, everyday example of a limiting reactant was used in the reference you consulted? If one was not used, give your own example.

   (c) What chemical example of a limiting reactant was used in the reference you consulted? If one was not used, give your own example.

3. (a) In this experiment you will filter your synthesized aspirin product from the reaction mixture using vacuum filtration. Find information in your textbook, a laboratory manual, or a Web site about vacuum filtration. Cite your reference.

(b) Sketch the apparatus for a vacuum filtration. Label each piece of equipment.

(c) Why is it called vacuum filtration?

(d) When transferring the reaction mixture to the funnel, is it better (1) to swirl the mixture and transfer a slurry of solution and aspirin, or (2) to let the aspirin settle and transfer the bulk of the solution first? Briefly explain.

4. **(a)** Write a balanced chemical equation for the acid catalyzed reaction of salicylic acid and acetic anhydride to make aspirin and acetic acid. Indicate the physical state of each reactant and product, using the abbreviations: (aq) for aqueous solution, (s) for solid, (ℓ) for liquid, and (g) for gas.

(b) Draw the chemical structure for the reactants and products.

5. Find a chemical supply catalog in either hard copy or on the World Wide Web. (Ask your laboratory instructor if you are to use a particular chemical company.) What is the cost of the smallest unit of ACS grade acetic anhydride and salicylic acid? Cite your reference.

6. **(a)** Examine a bottle of regular strength aspirin. How many grams of aspirin are in 10 tablets?

(b) How many milliliters of acetic anhydride are needed to make that much aspirin? (You need to know the density of acetic anhydride to answer this question.)

(c) How many grams of salicylic acid are needed to make that much aspirin?

(d) Using your answer to Pre-Laboratory Assignment **5**, how much will the acetic anhydride cost?

(e) Using your answer to Pre-Laboratory Assignment **5**, how much will the salicylic acid cost?

(f) Which should be your limiting reactant? Briefly explain.

7. A student in another laboratory section working on the Atkinson aspirin project synthesized some aspirin and determined its purity following the instructions in the Laboratory Investigations section of this experiment. Here is the data he collected:

mass of product sample titrated, g	0.301
concentration of sodium hydroxide, M	0.102
initial volume of sodium hydroxide, mL	4.89
final volume of sodium hydroxide, mL	19.32

(a) How many grams of aspirin are in the product sample titrated? (1 mol aspirin reacts with 1 mol sodium hydroxide.)

(b) What is the percent purity of the synthesized aspirin?

8. The Laboratory Investigations section of this experiment states you will determine the purity of your product by titration. No detailed procedure is given. Your laboratory instructor may provide one or ask you to outline the steps you will follow, using the Laboratory Investigations Outline page of this module. Find information in your textbook, a laboratory manual, or a Web site about titration. Cite your reference. You should write the outline in such a way that another student could use it to determine the product purity, without having to ask you any questions.

9. Because there is no data table provided for this experiment, your laboratory instructor may provide one. On the other hand, your laboratory instructor may ask you to:

   (a) determine which data you are going to collect, and

   (b) create a table to organize these data.

   If this is the case, organize and record your data on the Laboratory Investigations Data page for this module. Because not all of the measurements and observations you need to record may be obvious at first, leave plenty of space between the lines of your data table for data you may not have considered recording when you created the table.

LABORATORY INVESTIGATIONS

Reagents

acetic anhydride
salicylic acid
concentrated sulfuric acid

0.1*M* sodium hydroxide
95% ethanol
phenolphthalein

Special Equipment

aspirator
Büchner funnel
buret and buret clamp

filter flask
pressure tubing

CAUTION

Wear departmentally approved safety goggles at all times while in the chemistry laboratory.

Always use caution in the laboratory. Many chemicals are potentially harmful. Immediately tell your laboratory instructor if you spill any reagents.

When working with the boiling-water bath, be careful that you do not come in contact with the steam or the hot apparatus, and that you do not knock over the boiling-water bath. Use beaker tongs to handle the hot glassware.

NOTE: Record all data and observations on your Laboratory Investigations Data sheet.
Dispose of your aspirin, rinses, and titration solutions according to your laboratory instructor's directions.

1. *Synthesis of aspirin.* Prepare a boiling-water bath large enough to hold the Erlenmeyer flask that will serve as your reaction vessel.

CAUTION

Acetic anhydride is corrosive and a lachrymator. Salicylic acid is toxic and an irritant. Concentrated sulfuric acid is toxic and an oxidant.

Using the procedure recommended by your laboratory instructor, weigh the amount of salicylic acid you calculated in Pre-Laboratory Assignment 6(c) into a small Erlenmeyer flask. If the salicylic acid is the nonlimiting reactant use three times the mass you calculated. Add the amount of acetic anhydride you calculated in Pre-Laboratory Assignment 6(b). If the acetic anhydride is the nonlimiting reactant use three times the volume you calculated. Carefully add 5 drops of concentrated sulfuric acid. Gently, swirl the flask to mix thoroughly. Place the flask in your boiling-water bath and heat the contents for 15–20 min.

Prepare an ice-water bath large enough to hold the Erlenmeyer flask. Chill a wash bottle of distilled or deionized water in the ice-water bath.

Remove the flask from the boiling-water bath. In the *fume hood* slowly add, in 1- to 2-mL portions, 10 mL of chilled, distilled or deionized water. Carefully swirl the contents after each addition. Chill the Erlenmeyer flask in the ice-water bath for 10–15 min. Observe the crystallization of the aspirin product. Notify your laboratory instructor if your aspirin does not precipitate from the reaction mixture.

Assemble your vacuum filtration apparatus.

Add 25 mL of chilled, distilled water to the Erlenmeyer flask and swirl. Filter the aspirin product. Wash the residue with 15 mL of chilled, distilled water. Dry the solid by drawing air through the filter for at least 15 min.

Determine the mass of aspirin synthesized.

2. *Determination of purity.*

CAUTION

Sodium hydroxide is toxic and corrosive. 95% Ethanol is flammable.

Titrate your *dry* aspirin with a standardized sodium hydroxide solution. Use a 0.30- to 0.35-g sample of aspirin. Add 15 mL of 95% ethanol and dissolve completely before adding 50 mL of distilled or deionized water, and 2–3 drops of phenolphthalein indicator. The end point of the titration should persist for 20 s. Do additional titrations as directed by your laboratory instructor.

3. *Cleanup and disposal.* Dispose of aspirin and filtrate into the collection containers provided by your laboratory instructor. Pour the titration mixtures into the drain, diluting with a large amount of running water.

Wash all equipment with soap or detergent, rinse with tap water and then with distilled water, and dry.

CAUTION

Wash your hands thoroughly with soap or detergent before leaving the laboratory.

Name _____ Section _____ Date _____

Laboratory Investigations Outline

Laboratory Investigations Data

Name   Section   Date

Post-Laboratory Questions

(Use the spaces provided for the answers and additional paper if necessary.)

1. Calculate your mass percent yield of aspirin.

2. Calculate the percent purity of your aspirin.

3. Why was 95% ethanol added when titrating the aspirin?

4. Students in another laboratory section working on the Atkinson aspirin project made some technical errors while synthesizing their aspirin. Would these mistakes cause their calculated percent yield to be higher, lower, or the same as the actual percent yield? Briefly explain.

    (a) The aspirin was not completely dry before weighing the product.

    (b) Room temperature, not chilled, distilled water was used.

    (c) When the students weighed their salicylic acid, some of it missed the Erlenmeyer flask and fell onto the balance pan without them knowing it.

    (d) Less than the calculated amount of acetic anhydride was used.

5. On a separate sheet of paper, write a memorandum to the students in the marketing course that they can include in their cost analysis report to Atkinson Health Products. Your memo should address your choice of limiting and excess reactant, the ease or difficulty of synthesizing aspirin, your percent yield, your product purity, and your recommendation for pursuing or not pursuing this marketing venture from the standpoint of production.

6. (a) Based on a 60% yield, how much salicylic acid and acetic anhydride would Atkinson Health Products need to make one million 100-tablet bottles of regular aspirin?

   (b) Based on the prices you found for salicylic acid and acetic anhydride, how much would these two reactants for one million bottles of aspirin cost?

   (c) What additional production and marketing costs should Atkinson consider when making their decision to include aspirin in their product line?

Appendix 1

PROPERTIES OF SUBSTANCES

Substance	Formula	Formula Mass (g/mol)	Melting Point (°C)	Boiling Point (°C)	Density[1] (g/cm³)	Specific Heat J/g °	Price[2] ($/kg)
acetic acid	$C_2H_4O_2$	60.05	16.6	117.9	1.049	2.05	24
acetone	C_3H_6O	58.08	-95.3	56.2	0.790	2.18	20
acetonitrile	C_2H_3N	41.05	-45.7	81.6	0.786	2.26	36
acetophenone	C_8H_8O	120.16	20.5	202.0	1.028	1.98	26
aluminum	Al	26.98	660.2	2467	2.702	0.900	50
aluminum chloride	$AlCl_3$	133.34	183	190	2.44	0.787	60
ammonia	NH_3	17.03	-77.7	-33.3		2.19	
benzene	C_6H_6	78.12	5.5	80.1	0.879	1.74	34
benzoic acid	$C_7H_6O_2$	122.13	122.4	249	1.26	1.20	32
1-butanol	$C_4H_{10}O$	74.12	-89.5	117.2	0.810	2.3	25
2-butanol	$C_4H_{10}O$	74.12	-115	99.5	0.808		24
i-butyl alcohol	$C_4H_{10}O$	74.12	-108	108	0.803		30
t-butyl alcohol	$C_4H_{10}O$	74.12	25.5	82.2	0.789	3.0	36
calcium chloride	$CaCl_2$	110.99	772		2.15	0.686	63
carbon tetrachloride	CCl_4	153.82	-23.0	76.5	1.594	0.86	161
chloroform	$CHCl_3$	119.38	-63.5	61.7	1.483	0.97	26
chromium	Cr	52.00	1890	2482	7.20	0.449	200
copper	Cu	63.55	1083	2595	8.92	0.385	61
cyclohexane	C_6H_{12}	84.16	6.55	80.7	0.779	1.8	30
cyclohexanol	$C_6H_{12}O$	100.16	25.1	161.1	0.962	1.74	20
ethanol	C_2H_6O	46.07	-117	78.5	0.789	2.45	30
ethyl acetate	$C_4H_8O_2$	88.12	-83.6	77.1	0.900	1.93	30
ethyl ether	$C_4H_{10}O$	74.12	-116.2	34.5	0.714	2.32	36
glucose	$C_6H_{12}O_6$	180.16	146d		1.544	1.15	29
gold	Au	196.97	1064	2807	19.3	0.129	100000
gold(III) chloride	$AuCl_3$	303.33		229	3.9		80000
hexane	C_6H_{14}	86.18	-95	69.0	0.660	2.26	44
hydrogen chloride	HCl	36.46	-114.8	-84.9	1×10^{-3}	0.81	

Substance	Formula	Formula Mass (g/mol)	Melting Point (°C)	Boiling Point (°C)	Density[1] (g/cm³)	Specific Heat J/g °	Price[2] ($/kg)
iodine	I_2	253.81	113.5	184.4	4.93	0.22	180
iron	Fe	55.85	1535	3000	7.86	0.451	64
lauric acid	$C_{12}H_{24}O_2$	200.33	44	131	0.869		20
lead	Pb	207.19	327.5	1744	11.29	0.129	36
magnesium	Mg	24.31	651	1107	1.74	1.02	90
maple wood	$(C_6H_{12}O_6)_n$				0.68		
mercury	Hg	200.59	-38.9	357	13.59	0.139	113
methanol	CH_4O	32.04	-93.9	65.0	0.791	2.51	22
methylene chloride	CH_2Cl_2	84.93	-95.1	40	1.327	1.20	27
pentane	C_5H_{12}	72.15	-129.7	36.1	0.626		46
phenyl carbonate	$C_{13}H_{10}O_3$	214.2	83	306			47
platinum	Pt	195.09	1772	3827	21.4	0.133	100000
potassium	K	39.10	63.6	774	0.86	0.753	1200
potassium chloride	KCl	74.56	776		1.490	0.68	56
1-propanol	C_3H_8O	60.11	-126.5	97.4	0.804	2.39	28
2-propanol	C_3H_8O	60.11	-89.5	82.4	0.786	2.58	22
salicylic acid	$C_7H_6O_3$	138.12	159	211	1.443		80
silver	Ag	107.87	960.8	2212	10.5	0.236	2400
silver chloride	AgCl	143.32	455	1550	5.56	0.36	2200
sodium	Na	22.99	97.8	883	0.97	1.23	78
sodium chloride	NaCl	58.44	801	1413	2.165	0.866	32
sodium hydroxide	NaOH	40.00	318.4	1390	2.130		58
tin	Sn	118.69	231.9	2260	7.30	0.22	180
titanium	Ti	47.90	1675	3260	4.5	0.523	121
toluene	C_7H_8	92.15	-95	110.6	0.867	1.69	23
tungsten	W	183.85	3410	5660	19.4	0.135	120
vanillin	$C_8H_8O_3$	152.16	81	285	1.056		84
water	H_2O	18.02	0.00	100.0	0.998	4.184	21 (HPLC)
zinc	Zn	65.37	419.4	907	7.14	0.387	56

[1]20°C

[2]very approximate price from 2004 *Aldrich Catalog* (grade and purity dependent).

Appendix 2

COMMON IONS BY CHARGE

A. Positive Ions

1+

Ammonium	NH_4^+	Mercury(I) (mercurous)	Hg_2^{2+}
Copper(I) (cuprous)	Cu^+	Potassium	K^+
Hydrogen	H^+	Silver	Ag^+
Hydronium	H_3O^+	Sodium	Na^+
Lithium	Li^+		

2+

Barium	Ba^{2+}	Magnesium	Mg^{2+}
Cadmium	Cd^{2+}	Manganese(II) (manganous)	Mn^{2+}
Calcium	Ca^{2+}	Mercury(II) (mercuric)	Hg^{2+}
Cobalt(II) (cobaltous)	Co^{2+}	Nickel(II) (nickelous)	Ni^{2+}
Copper(II) (cupric)	Cu^{2+}	Strontium	Sr^{2+}
Iron(II) (ferrous)	Fe^{2+}	Tin(II) (stannous)	Sn^{2+}
Lead(II) (plumbous)	Pb^{2+}	Zinc	Zn^{2+}

3+

Aluminum	Al^{3+}	Cerium(III) (cerous)	Ce^{3+}
Antimony(III)	Sb^{3+}	Chromium(III) (chromic)	Cr^{3+}
Arsenic(III)	As^{3+}	Iron(III) (ferric)	Fe^{3+}
Bismuth(III)	Bi^{3+}		

4+

| Lead(IV) (plumbic) | Pb^{4+} | Tin(IV) (stannic) | Sn^{4+} |

5+

| Antimony(V) | Sb^{5+} | Bismuth(V) | Bi^{5+} |
| Arsenic(V) | As^{5+} | | |

COMMON IONS BY CHARGE continued

B. Negative ions

<u>1-</u>

Acetate	$C_2H_3O_2^-$	Hydrogen sulfate (bisulfate)	HSO_4^-
Bromate	BrO_3^-	Hydrogen sulfite (bisulfite)	HSO_3^-
Bromide	Br^-	Hydroxide	OH^-
Chlorate	ClO_3^-	Hypochlorite	ClO^-
Chloride	Cl^-	Iodate	IO_3^-
Chlorite	ClO_2^-	Iodide	I^-
Cyanate	NCO^-	Nitrate	NO_3^-
Cyanide	CN^-	Nitrite	NO_2^-
Fluoride	F^-	Perchlorate	ClO_4^-
Hydride	H^-	Permanganate	MnO_4^-
Hydrogen carbonate (bicarbonate)	HCO_3^-	Thiocyanate	SCN^-

<u>2-</u>

Carbonate	CO_3^{2-}	Sulfate	SO_4^{2-}
Chromate	CrO_4^{2-}	Sulfide	S^{2-}
Dichromate	$Cr_2O_7^{2-}$	Sulfite	SO_3^{2-}
Oxalate	$C_2O_4^{2-}$	Tetrathionate	$S_4O_6^{2-}$
Oxide	O^{2-}	Thiosulfate	$S_2O_3^{2-}$
Persulfate	$S_2O_8^{2-}$		

<u>3-</u>

Ferricyanide	$Fe(CN)_6^{3-}$	Phosphate	PO_4^{3-}

<u>4-</u>

Ferrocyanide	$Fe(CN)_6^{4-}$

Appendix 3

SOLUBILITIES OF IONIC COMPOUNDS - APPROXIMATE # OF GRAMS OF SOLUTE PER 100 GRAMS OF SOLUTION

	$C_2H_3O_2^-$	Br^-	CO_3^{2-}	Cl^-	CrO_4^{2-}	$Fe(CN)_6^{3-}$	$Fe(CN)_6^{4-}$	OH^-	IO_3^-	I^-	NO_3^-	$C_2O_4^{2-}$	PO_4^{3-}	SO_4^{2-}	S^{2-}	SCN^-
Al^{3+}	ss	s		31			ss	1×10^{-4}		s,d	42	i	i	27	d	
NH_4^+	60	43	50	27	25	vs	s	47	2	63	66	4	26	43	vs	63
Ba^{2+}	42	51	2×10^{-3}	26	4×10^{-4}		.1	4	.02	68	8	2×10^{-2}	i	2×10^{-4}	d	26
Ca^{2+}	26	59	6×10^{-3}	43	14		36	.16	.3	68	56	7×10^{-4}	2×10^{-3}	.2	.02	s
Ce^{3+}	20	3	i	50				i	.1	s	64	4×10^{-5}	i	9	i	
Co^{2+}	s	54	i	35	i	i	i	3×10^{-4}	1	65	50	3×10^{-3}	i	26	4×10^{-4}	51
Cu^{2+}	7	56	i	42	i	i	i	3×10^{-4}	.1	1.1	55	2×10^{-3}	i	17	2×10^{-4}	d
Fe^{3+}		s		70			i	1×10^{-5}	.04	vs	46		i	ss	3×10^{-17}	vs
Pb^{2+}	31	.8	1×10^{-4}	1	7×10^{-6}	ss	i	.02	2×10^{-3}	.07	35	1×10^{-4}	1×10^{-5}	4×10^{-3}	9×10^{-5}	.05
Li^+	31	62	1.3	45	50			11	45	62	43	7	.03	26	vs	vs
Mg^{2+}	40	50	.07	35	42		25	2×10^{-3}	8	58	41	.03	.02	28	d	
K^+	70	40	52	25	39	31	23	53	7.5	59	27	26	47	10	s	67
Ag^+	1.0	8×10^{-6}	3×10^{-3}	2×10^{-4}	4×10^{-3}	7×10^{-5}	i		4×10^{-3}	3×10^{-6}	70	3×10^{-3}	6×10^{-4}	.8	7×10^{-13}	2×10^{-5}
Na^+	32	48	22	26.4	47	23	15	52	8	64	47	3.3	11	20	16	58
Sr^{2+}	27	51	1×10^{-3}	35	.12	33		1	.03	64	42	5×10^{-3}	i	.01	s,d	vs
Zn^{2+}	25	82	2×10^{-2}	79	i	i	i	4×10^{-4}	.9	83	56	7×10^{-4}	i	30	10^{-8}	s

An arbitrary standard for solubility is that a compound is called soluble if at least 1 gram dissolves in 100 mL of solution.

When quantitative data could not be located, the symbols below were used:

vs = very soluble, s = soluble, ss = slightly soluble, i = insoluble, d = decomposes

Appendix 4

Solutions to Starred Prelaboratory Problems

Experiment 1

3. Vinegar is a polar liquid and oil is nonpolar. The attractions between molecules of each liquid are much stronger than the attractions to molecules of the other liquid thus they would rather keep to themselves than mix in this case.

5. The small diameter neck minimizes the error caused by a slight missetting of the water level.

7. a. substance, element
   b. homogeneous mixture, unsaturated solution
   c. heterogeneous mixture
   d. extensive physical property
   e. Intensive physical property
   f. homogeneous mixture, unsaturated solution

Experiment 2

1. a. $\left(\dfrac{55.428 - 54.730}{61.945 - 54.730}\right)(100\%) = 9.67\%$

   b. $\left(\dfrac{0.33}{10.00}\right)(100\%) = 3.3\%$

   c. Neither filtration or recrystallization would give any information about the mass percent of dissolved potassium chloride in the solution.

   d. As saturation is attained at about 25% by mass KCl and the solution was only 9.67%, the solution was not saturated.

Experiment 3

1. a. 4, 3, 4, 2, 3

3. a. Salt lowers the freezing point of the now salt water. Therefore addition of salt to the roads often lowers the freezing point of the salt water to a temperature below prevailing temperatures thus preventing the freezing of the salt water solution.

4. a. $\left(\dfrac{1.8}{2.5}\right)(100\%) = 72\%$

   b. The melting range is broad and depressed considerably from the literature value indicating the presence of significant amounts of impurity (~4%).

   c. As the literature value for the melting point of naphthalene is 80.55°C and the recrystallized sample melted over a narrow range almost identical to the literature value, the recrystallization substantially purified the sample.

Experiment 3 (continued)

6. $V = (4/3)\pi r^3 = (4/3)(3.1416)(1.85/2)^3 \text{ cm}^3 = 3.32 \text{ cm}^3$

$d = \dfrac{15.00 \text{ g}}{3.31 \text{ cm}^3} = 4.52 \text{ g/cm}^3$ This value is very close to the literature value for titanium.

Experiment 4

1. a. $\underline{\text{balance 1}}$ average $= (45.747 + 45.745 + 45.748)/3 = 45.747 \text{ g}$
    average deviation $= (0.000 + 0.002 + 0.001)/3 = \underline{0.001}$

2. a. $\dfrac{64.859 \text{ g} - 37.234 \text{ g}}{25.00 \text{ mL}} = 1.105 \text{ g/mL}$

Experiment 5

1. a. $2 \text{ Al}_{(s)} + 3/2 \text{ O}_{2(g)} = \text{Al}_2\text{O}_{3(s)}$

    b. $(5.0 \text{ g Al})\left(\dfrac{1 \text{ mol Al}}{27.0 \text{ g Al}}\right)\left(\dfrac{1 \text{ mol Al}_2\text{O}_3}{2 \text{ mol Al}}\right)\left(\dfrac{102.0 \text{ g Al}_2\text{O}_3}{1 \text{ mol Al}_2\text{O}_3}\right) = 9.44 \text{ g Al}_2\text{O}_3$

    $(5.0 \text{ g O}_2)\left(\dfrac{1 \text{ mol O}_2}{32.0 \text{ g O}_2}\right)\left(\dfrac{1 \text{ mol Al}_2\text{O}_3}{3/2 \text{ mol O}_2}\right)\left(\dfrac{102.0 \text{ g Al}_2\text{O}_3}{1 \text{ mol Al}_2\text{O}_3}\right) = 10.6 \text{ g Al}_2\text{O}_3$ $\therefore$ Al is limiting reagent and 9.44 g of Al_2O_3 will be formed.

    $(9.44 \text{ g Al}_2\text{O}_3)\left(\dfrac{1 \text{ mol Al}_2\text{O}_3}{102 \text{ g Al}_2\text{O}_3}\right)\left(\dfrac{3/2 \text{ mol O}_2}{1 \text{ mol Al}_2\text{O}_3}\right)\left(\dfrac{32.0 \text{ g O}_2}{1 \text{ mol O}_2}\right) = 4.44 \text{ g O}_2$ reacted and 0.56 g O_2 are left

3. a. $\text{BaCl}_2 \cdot 2\text{H}_2\text{O}_{(s)} \xrightarrow{\Delta} \text{BaCl}_{2(s)} + 2 \text{ H}_2\text{O}_{(l)}$

4. a. $\left(\dfrac{2 \text{ mol H}_2\text{O}}{1 \text{ mol BaCl}_2 \cdot 2\text{H}_2\text{O}}\right)\left(\dfrac{18.02 \text{ g H}_2\text{O}}{1 \text{ mol H}_2\text{O}}\right)\left(\dfrac{1 \text{ mol BaCl}_2 \cdot 2\text{H}_2\text{O}}{244.2 \text{ g BaCl}_2 \cdot 2\text{H}_2\text{O}}\right)(100\%) = 14.76\%$

5. Assume 100.0 g of sample

    $(8.74 \text{ g C})\left(\dfrac{1 \text{ mole}}{12.011 \text{ g}}\right) = 0.727 \text{ moles C}$

    $(77.73 \text{ g Cl})\left(\dfrac{1 \text{ mole}}{35.453 \text{ g}}\right) = 2.192 \text{ moles Cl}$

    $(13.83 \text{ g F})\left(\dfrac{1 \text{ mole}}{19.00 \text{ g}}\right) = 0.728 \text{ moles F}$

    empirical formula $= \text{CCl}_3\text{F}$ $137/137 = 1$ molecular formula $= \text{CCl}_3\text{F}$

8. $\left(\dfrac{0.793 \text{ g H}_2\text{O}}{4.00 \text{ g}}\right)(100\%) = 19.8\%$ water

    $(0.793 \text{ g H}_2\text{O})\left(\dfrac{1 \text{ mol H}_2\text{O}}{18.02 \text{ g H}_2\text{O}}\right) = 0.0441 \text{ mol H}_2\text{O}$

    $[(4.00 - 0.793) \text{ g NiBr}_2]\left(\dfrac{1 \text{ mole NiBr}_2}{218.5 \text{ g NiBr}_2}\right) = 0.0147 \text{ mol NiBr}_2$

    $\left(\dfrac{0.0441 \text{ mol H}_2\text{O}}{0.0147 \text{ mol NiBr}_2}\right) = 3.00 \text{ moles H}_2\text{O}/1 \text{ mole NiBr}_2$ Therefore the formula is $\text{NiBr}_2 \cdot 3\text{H}_2\text{O}$.

Experiment 6

1. | **reaction** | **classification** |

a. $Mg(s) + ZnCl_2(aq) = MgCl_2(aq) + Zn(s)$ SR

b. $2\,AgNO_3(aq) + CaCl_2(aq) = 2\,AgCl(s) + Ca(NO_3)_2(aq)$ DR

c. $C_2H_6(g) + 7/2\,O_2(g) = 2\,CO_2(g) + 3\,H_2O(g)$ CU

d. $Na_2O(s) + H_2O(l) = 2\,NaOH(aq)$ CA

e. $KClO_3(s) = KCl(s) + 3/2\,O_2(g)$ D

2. a. $BaCl_2(aq) + Na_2SO_4(aq) = BaSO_4(s) + 2\,NaCl(aq)$ DR

b. $2\,Fe(s) + 3\,CuCl_2(aq) = 2\,FeCl_3(aq) + 3\,Cu(s)$ SR

c. $C_6H_6(l) + 15/2\,O_2(g) = 6\,CO_2(g) + 3\,H_2O(g)$ CU

d. $BaCl_2(s) + 2\,H_2O(l) = BaCl_2 \cdot 2H_2O(s)$ CA

3. a. $N_2(g) + 3\,H_2(g) = 2\,NH_3(g)$

b. $\dfrac{1\ \text{mole}\ N_2}{3\ \text{moles}\ H_2}$

Experiment 7

1. a. $(33\ g)\left(\dfrac{1\ \text{mole}}{44.0\ g}\right) = 0.75\ \text{moles}$

2. a. $(3.45 \times 10^{-2}\ \text{moles})\left(\dfrac{169.9\ g}{1\ \text{mole}}\right) = 5.86\ g$

3. a. $Mg(NO_3)_2(aq) + 2\,NaOH(s) = Mg(OH)_2(s) + 2\,NaNO_3(aq)$

4. $2\,Na(s) + 2\,H_2O(l) = 2\,NaOH(aq) + H_2(g)$

$(2.3\ g\ Na)\left(\dfrac{1\ \text{mol Na}}{23.0\ g\ Na}\right)\left(\dfrac{1\ \text{mol}\ H_2}{2\ \text{mol Na}}\right)\left(\dfrac{2.01\ g\ H_2}{1\ \text{mol}\ H_2}\right) = 0.10\ g\ H_2$ (theoretical yield)

$\left(\dfrac{0.080\ g}{0.10\ g}\right)(100\%) = 80\%$ (percent yield)

Experiment 9

1. Barium sulfate is very insoluble in water and not enough is absorbed into the body to cause a problem.

3. a. If sodium sulfate is used in the first step, marginally soluble silver sulfate might precipitate along with the barium sulfate.

Experiment 10

1. b. copper(II) hydroxide

2. a. K>Al>Pb>Ag

   b. $Al_{(s)} + 3 Ag^+ = Al^{3+} + 3 Ag_{(s)}$

2. a. $Cu_{(s)} + 2 Ag^+ = Cu^{2+} + 2 Ag_{(s)}$

   b. As the copper replaces the silver, it is more active than silver.

   c. Copper loses 2 electrons in the process (its oxidation number increases by 2) therefore it is oxidized.

Experiment 11

3. a. $(5.00 \times 10^{-2} \text{ L CuSO}_4 \cdot 5H_2O)\left(\dfrac{0.75 \text{ moles CuSO}_4 \cdot 5H_2O}{1 \text{ L CuSO}_4 \cdot 5H_2O}\right)\left(\dfrac{249.68 \text{ g CuSO}_4 \cdot 5H_2O}{1 \text{ mole CuSO}_4 \cdot 5H_2O}\right) = 9.36 \text{ g } \underline{CuSO_4 \cdot 5H_2O}$

4. $AgNO_{3(aq)} + HCl_{(aq)} = HNO_{3(aq)} + AgCl_{(s)}$

   $\left(\dfrac{8.50 \times 10^{-3} \text{ L HCl}}{1.000 \times 10^{-2} \text{ L AgNO}_3}\right)\left(\dfrac{0.1100 \text{ mol HCl}}{1 \text{ L solution}}\right)\left(\dfrac{1 \text{ mol AgNO}_3}{1 \text{ mol HCl}}\right) = 0.0935 \text{ M AgNO}_3$

7. The indicator is selected so that there is a visual change as close as possible to the point where stoichiometric amounts of the two reactants have been used.

Experiment 12

1. b. The temperature change extrapolated to 3.5 min. is 32.7 °C − 18.2 °C = 14.5 °C.

2. $C_u = -\dfrac{(25.00 \text{ g H}_2O)(4.184 \text{ J/g deg})(5.5 \text{ deg})}{(15.00 \text{ g unk})(-72.5 \text{ deg})} = 0.529 \text{ J/g deg}$

   atomic mass = 25/0.529 = 47.2 g/mol   This value indicates that the unknown is titanium.

Experiment 14

1. As $E = hc/\lambda$, the longer the wavelength, the lower the energy. Microwaves with $\lambda \approx 0.01$ cm have a much longer wavelength than visible light with wavelengths between 4×10^{-5} and 7×10^{-5} cm.

2. a. $(5.00 \times 10^{-2} \text{ L CuSO}_4 \cdot 5\text{H}_2\text{O}) \left(\dfrac{0.30 \text{ moles CuSO}_4 \cdot 5\text{H}_2\text{O}}{1 \text{ L CuSO}_4 \cdot 5\text{H}_2\text{O}} \right) \left(\dfrac{249.68 \text{ g CuSO}_4 \cdot 5\text{H}_2\text{O}}{1 \text{ mole CuSO}_4 \cdot 5\text{H}_2\text{O}} \right) = 3.8 \text{ g CuSO}_4 \cdot 5\text{H}_2\text{O}$

   b. $M_1V_1 = M_2V_2$ $2/5(0.30) = 0.12$ M

4. a. $-\log_{10}T = A = \epsilon bc$ $-\log_{10}(0.59) = \epsilon(1)(0.25)$ $\epsilon = 0.92$

5. Absorption and wavelength are not linearly related and a plot of absorption vs wavelength usually gives bell shaped curves if an absorption occurs in the wavelength region.

   Absorption at one wavelength is related to the concentration of the absorbing species by Beer's law, $A = \epsilon bc$. As ϵ and b are constants for a given absorbing species at a given wavelength, A is proportional to the concentration and a plot of A vs c should yield a straight line.

Experiment 16

1. a. HF because it has hydrogen bonding. Both have same number of electrons.

   d. SiH_4 has more electrons and at the same temperature, a lower molecular velocity.

2. a. NaCl is an ionic compound and is more soluble in the polar solvent, water.

Experiment 17

2. a. $V = \dfrac{nRT}{P} = \dfrac{(1 \text{ mol})(0.08206 \text{ L·atm/mol·K})(273 \text{ K})}{1 \text{ atm}} = 22.4 \text{ L/mol}$

5. $Mg(s) + 2 HCl(aq) = MgCl_2(aq) + H_2(g)$

   $(0.525 \text{ g Mg}) \left(\dfrac{1 \text{ mol Mg}}{24.31 \text{ g Mg}} \right) \left(\dfrac{1 \text{ mol H}_2}{1 \text{ mol Mg}} \right) = 2.16 \times 10^{-2} \text{ moles H}_2$

   $V = \dfrac{nRT}{P} = \dfrac{(2.16 \times 10^{-2})(0.08206)(300)}{752/760} = 0.537 \text{ L H}_2$

Experiment 18

2. a. $\Delta T_{emp} = mK_f$ $K_f = \dfrac{\Delta T_{emp}}{m} = \dfrac{(3.4 \text{ deg})(5.00 \times 10^{-3} \text{ kg})}{(0.38 \text{ g}/154.2 \text{ g·mol}^{-1})} = 6.9 \dfrac{\text{deg·kg}}{\text{mol}}$

   b. $\Delta T_{emp} = mK_f = \left(\dfrac{0.150 \text{ g C}_{14}\text{H}_{10}}{3.00 \times 10^{-3} \text{ kg}} \right) \left(\dfrac{1 \text{ mole C}_{14}\text{H}_{10}}{178.24 \text{ g C}_{14}\text{H}_{10}} \right) \left(\dfrac{6.9 \text{ deg·kg}}{\text{mol}} \right) = 1.94 \,^\circ\text{C}$

   $216^\circ\text{C} - 1.9^\circ\text{C} = 214^\circ\text{C}$

Experiment 18 (continued)

4. $V = \left(\dfrac{1\,cm^3}{8.90\,g}\right)\left(\dfrac{58.7\,g}{1\,mole}\right)\left(\dfrac{1\,mole}{6.022 \times 10^{23}\,atoms}\right)\left(\dfrac{4\,atoms}{unit\,cell}\right) = 4.38 \times 10^{-23}\,cm^3$

The edge of the unit cell (a) is the cube root of the volume $[V^{1/3}]$

$a = V^{1/3} = (4.38 \times 10^{-23}\,cm^3)^{1/3} = (43.8 \times 10^{-24}\,cm^3)^{1/3} = 3.52 \times 10^{-8}\,cm$

atomic radius $= r = a \times 2^{1/2}/4 = (3.52 \times 10^{-8}\,cm)(0.354) = 1.24 \times 10^{-8}\,cm$

Experiment 19

3. $\left(\dfrac{5.00 \times 10^{-3}\,moles}{1\,L}\right)\left(\dfrac{1\,L}{10^3\,mL}\right)\left(\dfrac{mL\,EDTA}{mL\,H_2O}\right)\left(\dfrac{1\,mol\,Ca^{2+}}{1\,mol\,EDTA}\right)\left(\dfrac{100\,g\,CaCO_3}{1\,mol\,CaCO_3}\right)(10^6\,ppm) = \dfrac{500\,(mL\,EDTA)}{mL\,H_2O}$

Experiment 21

1. b. $(1.1\,g\,KHP)\left(\dfrac{1\,mole\,KHP}{204.22\,g\,KHP}\right)\left(\dfrac{1\,mole\,NaOH}{1\,mole\,KHP}\right)\left(\dfrac{1\,L\,NaOH}{0.25\,moles}\right) = 0.022\,L = 22\,mL\,NaOH\,soln.$

2. $\left(\dfrac{0.4904\,g\,KHP}{0.02382\,L\,NaOH}\right)\left(\dfrac{1\,mol\,KHP}{204.2\,g\,KHP}\right)\left(\dfrac{1\,mol\,NaOH}{1\,mol\,KHP}\right) = 0.1008\,moles\,NaOH/L\,soln.$

Experiment 22

1. $\left(\dfrac{0.03122\,L\,NaOH}{0.02500\,L\,H_2SO_4}\right)\left(\dfrac{0.1234\,mol\,NaOH}{1\,L\,NaOH}\right)\left(\dfrac{1\,mol\,H_2SO_4}{2\,mol\,NaOH}\right) = 7.705 \times 10^{-2}\,M\,H_2SO_4$

2. $\left(\dfrac{0.01628\,L\,NaOH}{0.01000\,L\,vin.}\right)\left(\dfrac{0.5120\,mol\,NaOH}{1\,L}\right)\left(\dfrac{1\,mol\,acetic\,acid}{1\,mol\,NaOH}\right) = 0.8335\,M\,acetic\,acid$

$\left(\dfrac{0.8335\,mol\,acetic\,acid}{1\,L\,soln.}\right)\left(\dfrac{0.01000\,L\,soln.}{10.05\,g\,soln.}\right)\left(\dfrac{60.05\,g\,acetic\,acid}{1\,mol\,acetic\,acid}\right)(100\%) = 4.98\%\,acetic\,acid$

3. $(.01556\,L\,NaOH)(0.1020\,mol\,NaOH/L)(1\,mol\,HX/1\,mol\,NaOH) = 1.587 \times 10^{-3}\,mol\,HX$

$0.1936\,g/1.587 \times 10^{-3}\,mol = 122.0\,g/mol$

Experiment 23

1.

	pH	$[H^+]$ (M)	$[OH^-]$ (M)	pOH
a.	4.7	2×10^{-5}	5×10^{-10}	9.3
b.	2.11	7.7×10^{-3}	1.3×10^{-12}	11.89

6. $H_2S_{(aq)} = H^+ + SH^-$

$[H^+] = [SH^-] = 1.0 \times 10^{-4}\,M,\ [H_2S] = 1.0 \times 10^{-1} - 1.0 \times 10^{-4} = 1.0 \times 10^{-1}\,M$

$K_a = \dfrac{[H^+][SH^-]}{[H_2S]} = \dfrac{(1.0 \times 10^{-4})^2}{0.10} = 1.0 \times 10^{-7}$

Experiment 24

3. $(0.300 \text{ mol HCl/L})(0.0250 \text{ L}) = 7.50\times10^{-3} \text{ moles HCl (total)}$

    $(0.200 \text{ mol NaOH/L})(0.0248 \text{ L}) = 4.96\times10^{-3} \text{ moles NaOH}$

    $(4.96\times10^{-3} \text{ moles NaOH})(1 \text{ mol HCl/1 mol NaOH}) = 4.96\times10^{-3} \text{ moles HCl (excess)}$

    $7.50\times10^{-3} - 4.96\times10^{-3} = 2.54\times10^{-3} \text{ moles HCl consumed by carbonate}$

    $\left(\dfrac{1 \text{ mol BaCO}_3}{2 \text{ mol HCl}}\right)(2.54\times10^{-3} \text{ mol HCl}) = 1.27\times10^{-3} \text{ moles BaCO}_3$

    $0.250 \text{ g}/1.27\times10^{-3} \text{ mol} = 197 \text{ g/mol}$

    Use of the periodic table to determine the formula mass of $BaCO_3$ yields 197.3 g/mol. The agreement well within experimental error strongly supports the conclusion that the product was barium carbonate.

Experiment 26

1. a. $\Delta G° = \Delta H° - T\Delta S° = 25.7 \text{ kJ/mol} - (298 \text{ K})(0.1087 \text{ kJ/mol·K}) = -6.69 \text{ kJ/mol}$

    $\Delta G° = -RT\ln K$

    $\ln K = -\Delta G°/RT = \dfrac{-(-6700 \text{ J/mol})}{(8.313 \text{ J/mol·K})(298 \text{ K})} = 2.70$

    $K = 14.9$

    b. Endothermic

    c. The positive ΔS is consistent with the increase in disorder that occurs when a solid dissolves in a liquid.

Experiment 27

1. a. $K_{sp} = [\text{Ag}^+][\text{Br}^-] = 5\times10^{-13}$

    $K_f = \dfrac{[\text{Ag(NH}_3)_2{}^+]}{[\text{Ag}^+][\text{NH}_3]^2} = 1.7\times10^7$

    $K_f K_{sp} = \dfrac{[\text{Ag(NH}_3)_2{}^+][\text{Br}^-]}{[\text{NH}_3]^2} = 8.5\times10^{-6} = \dfrac{(x)(0.01)}{(6.0)^2}$

    $x = 0.031 \text{ M}$ As the complex concentration comes out greater than 0.01 M, the silver bromide would dissolve.

Experiment 28

1. a. $\dfrac{\Delta[A]}{\Delta t} = \dfrac{2\Delta[P]}{\Delta t}$

2. a. $\dfrac{\Delta[P]}{\Delta t} = k[A][B]$ slow step $A + B \rightarrow I_{ntermediate}$

     fast step $I + B \rightarrow P$

Experiment 29

1. $(12 \text{ g SA}) \left(\dfrac{1 \text{ mol SA}}{138 \text{ g SA}} \right) \left(\dfrac{1 \text{ mol Asp}}{1 \text{ mol SA}} \right) \left(\dfrac{180 \text{ g Asp}}{1 \text{ mol Asp}} \right) = \begin{array}{l} 15.7 \text{ g Aspirin} \\ \text{(theoretical yield)} \end{array}$

     $(11/15.7)(100\%) = 70\%$ (percent yield)

3. c. $Ca(NO_3)_2(aq) + K_2C_2O_4(aq) = CaC_2O_4(s) + 2 KNO_3(aq)$

     As calcium oxalate is insoluble, equal volumes of only approximately equal molar solutions of calcium nitrate and potassium oxalate should be mixed and the product collected by vacuum filtration.

Experiment 30

1. a. 2, 4, 7

2. a. $Al(s) = Al^{3+} + 3 e^-$

     $3 H^+ + 3 e^- = 3/2 H_2(g)$

     $Al(s) + 3 H^+ = Al^{3+} + 3/2 H_2(g)$

5. $\left(\dfrac{0.800 \text{ g K}_3\text{Fe(CN)}_6}{1.90 \times 10^{-2} \text{ L Na}_2\text{S}_2\text{O}_3} \right) \left(\dfrac{1 \text{ mol K}_3\text{Fe(CN)}_6}{329.3 \text{ g K}_3\text{Fe(CN)}_6} \right) \left(\dfrac{1 \text{ mol Na}_2\text{S}_2\text{O}_3}{1 \text{ mol K}_3\text{Fe(CN)}_6} \right) = 0.128 \text{ M NaS}_2\text{O}_3$

Experiment 31

1. a. $C_2O_4^{2-} = 2\,CO_{2(g)} + 2\,e^-$

    $MnO_4^- + 8\,H^+ + 5\,e^- = Mn^{2+} + 4\,H_2O_{(g)}$

    $2\,MnO_4^- + 16\,H^+ + 5\,C_2O_4^{2-} = 2\,Mn^{2+} + 8\,H_2O_{(g)} + 10\,CO_{2(g)}$

    b. $\left(\dfrac{0.2600\text{ g Na}_2\text{C}_2\text{O}_4}{2.250\text{x}10^{-2}\text{ L KMnO}_4}\right)\left(\dfrac{1\text{ mol Na}_2\text{C}_2\text{O}_4}{134.00\text{ g Na}_2\text{C}_2\text{O}_4}\right)\left(\dfrac{2\text{ mol KMnO}_4}{5\text{ mol Na}_2\text{C}_2\text{O}_4}\right) = 0.03449$ M $KMnO_4$

    c. Permanganate is purple colored. During the titration, the permanganate reacts leaving the solution with little or no color. However, the slightest amount of permanganate beyond the stoichiometric amount will turn the solution purple.

3. $\left(\dfrac{0.02112\text{ L NaS}_2\text{O}_3}{0.00100\text{ L "Cl"}}\right)\left(\dfrac{0.150\text{ mol NaS}_2\text{O}_3}{1\text{ L NaS}_2\text{O}_3}\right)\left(\dfrac{1\text{ mol NaClO}}{2\text{ mol NaS}_2\text{O}_3}\right) = 1.584$ M NaClO

    $\left(\dfrac{1.584\text{ mol}}{\text{L soln.}}\right)\left(\dfrac{74.4\text{ g NaClO}}{1\text{ mol NaClO}}\right)\left(\dfrac{1\text{ L soln.}}{1180\text{ g soln}}\right)(100\%) = 9.99\%$

Experiment 32

1. a. $Cu_{(s)} + Sn^{4+} = Cu^{2+} + Sn^{2+}$ $\qquad\qquad$ $E° = -0.19$ volts

Experiment 33

1. $Pb_{(s)} + 2\,Ag^+ = Pb^{2+} + 2\,Ag_{(s)}$

2. 2.11 volts

3. $(1.5\text{x}10^{-2}\text{ coulombs/sec})(1.75\text{ hr})(3600\text{ sec/hr}) = 94.5$ coulombs

    $\left(\dfrac{94.5\text{ coul}}{0.108\text{ g Ag}}\right)\left(\dfrac{1\text{ electron}}{1.602\text{x}10^{-19}\text{ coul}}\right)\left(\dfrac{107.9\text{ g Ag}}{1\text{ mol Ag}}\right)\left(\dfrac{1\text{ atom Ag}}{1\text{ electron}}\right) = 5.89\text{x}10^{23}\ \dfrac{\text{atoms Ag}}{\text{mol Ag}}$

    $\left(\dfrac{94.5\text{ coulombs}}{0.108\text{ g Ag}}\right)\left(\dfrac{107.9\text{ g Ag}}{1\text{ mol Ag}}\right) = 9.4\text{x}10^4$ coulombs/mol

4. $(0.108\text{ g Ag})\left(\dfrac{1\text{ mol Ag}}{107.9\text{ g Ag}}\right)\left(\dfrac{1\text{ mol Pb}}{2\text{ mol Ag}}\right)\left(\dfrac{207.2\text{ g Pb}}{1\text{ mol Pb}}\right) = 0.104$ g Pb

Experiment 34

2. a. $(0.15\text{ M})(50/250) = 0.030$ M

    b. $A = \epsilon bc = (5.0)(1.00)(0.030) = 0.15$

CPSIA information can be obtained
at www.ICGtesting.com
Printed in the USA
FFHW020058160819
54331729-60022FF